The Learning Traveler Vol. 3

TEACHING ABROAD

Barbara Cahn Connotillo, Editor
with Walter Jackson

Special grant support from the U.S. Information Agency and Lilly Endowment, Inc. made publication of this book possible.

65019

INSTITUTE OF INTERNATIONAL EDUCATION
809 UNITED NATIONS PLAZA, NEW YORK, N.Y. 10017

ABOUT IIE

The Institute of International Education (IIE), a private nonprofit organization, is the oldest (founded 1919) and largest international educational agency in the United States. It has headquarters in New York City and a Washington, DC office; regional offices in Atlanta, Chicago, Denver, Houston, and San Francisco; and overseas offices in Zimbabwe (Harare), Hong Kong, Thailand (Bangkok), Indonesia (Jakarta), and Mexico (Mexico City).

IIE manages sponsored programs which assist 7,000 people each year through fellowships and grants. The Institute also conducts contribution-supported educational services, which include an information clearinghouse, student counseling, publications, and professional services to the campus study abroad adviser, foreign student adviser, and admissions officer. Contributions to the Institute are tax-deductible.

First edition.
Copyright © 1984 Institute of International Education.
All rights reserved.
Printed in the United States of America.
ISBN: 0-87206-124-8
Cover art by Kimble Mead.

CONTENTS

Introduction

Opportunities

V. EUROPE

VI. WESTERN HEMISPHERE

INTRODUCTION

INTRODUCTION

The Institute of International Education has, in recent years, seen increased evidence that U.S. educators—from elementary school teachers to university professors and from curriculum developers to school administrators—are interested in seeking employment opportunities abroad. This new, expanded, and revised edition of *Teaching Abroad* was prepared to better respond to these requests for information from recent graduates seeking their first teaching experience, seasoned professionals, and retired educators interested in a new and rewarding experience.

For those interested in teaching abroad, this publication will provide basic information on available opportunities. Naturally, we could not provide answers to *all* possible questions. We therefore strongly suggest that interested teachers contact specific organizations, agencies, or institutions for more detailed information.

No one-time job openings are listed. Instead, *Teaching Abroad* describes the scope of formal teacher exchange programs, faculty needs as reported by foreign governments, and the approximate number of faculty positions available annually within American and international schools abroad. It would have been impossible to survey each educational institution on all educational levels located abroad. In compiling this directory, a questionnaire survey was sent to a comprehensive mailing list of foreign government agencies, including Ministries of Education; U.S. government agencies; U.S. and foreign private organizations that sponsor formal teacher exchange programs; and American and international schools abroad, generally on the elementary and secondary level.

Additional sources of information can be found in the publications described in the annotated bibliography beginning on page 121. Often, international positions will also be advertised in newspapers of major metropolitan cities, such as *The New York Times* or *The Washington Post;* international periodicals like *The International Herald Tribune* and *The Times Higher Education Supplement;* educational trade press such as *The Chronicle of Higher Education;* and in the magazines and newsletters published by teachers' unions and educational associations.

There are many rewards, both personal and professional, for those who take teaching positions overseas. Many seek to do so in order to broaden their knowledge of particular subjects, deepen their understanding of other cultures, learn or perfect foreign languages, or gain new perspectives on teaching methods; others simply see overseas teaching as an adventure. What one gains depends on personal goals, expectations, and commitment.

Most teachers who spend time abroad do so for limited assignments of from one to three years. It is difficult to measure the benefits that U.S. education receives once these teachers return home. It is inevitable, however, that an international dimension will be brought into the U.S. classroom as a result of this overseas experience. And thus future students, as well as teachers themselves, will benefit from a greater international understanding of the world in which we live.

Opportunities for teaching abroad vary. Some may elect to engage in formal teacher exchanges whereby U.S. and foreign teachers simply switch positions and retain the salary and benefits from their home schools. Others may be employed directly by foreign governments to provide curriculum planning or to train the future teachers of their host country in what is known as teacher colleges. Others may choose to work in American or international schools abroad (often based on the U.S.-education model) and teach the dependents of U.S. and other foreign nationals employed overseas. In order to determine which might be the best choice, it is important to begin making detailed inquiries as far in advance of the desired move as possible.

While no concerted effort was made to describe student teaching positions abroad, some programs of this type are listed in this directory. Additional information on student teaching may be found in IIE's annual *The Learning Traveler* series, Volume 1: *U.S. College-Sponsored Programs Abroad: Academic Year* and Volume 2: *Vacation Study Abroad* (see Bibliography).

PRIOR TO DEPARTURE

Teaching abroad may also entail a dramatic change of lifestyle, and there are numerous factors one must consider before making a final decision on a particular assignment. It is important to bear in mind that there is a major difference between traveling abroad and working abroad.

The first major difference may be language. Limited knowlege of French, for example, may be sufficient for a week's vacation in Paris but grossly inadequate for a year's assignment in Ethiopia. Most institutions prefer that faculty possess as least a beginner's-level proficiency in the native language, even if the language utilized in the classroom is English. It would probably be a good idea to take some language classes before leaving the United States, and enrolling in a language institute upon arrival abroad can be helpful as well.

Before accepting teaching positions overseas, those interested should carefully examine their own personalities and their abilities to adapt to new situations, environments, people, and cultures. It is easy to underestimate the amount of adjustment required in such situations, and those best-suited for working abroad are those who adapt most easily to unfamiliar surroundings and customs.

Another consideration is whether or not to sever all ties with one's U.S. school or institution. Since many positions are short-term (one to two years), one option is to take an unpaid leave of absence. For shorter assignments (six months to one year), an alternative may be to take a sabbatical for that period of time. Either option would allow teachers to resume their current teaching positions upon their return. Prospective overseas teachers can look to their present schools and their unions or professional organizations for details on these or other alternatives.

Application Procedures

The need for careful planning cannot be emphasized enough, but timing may also be crucial. As a general rule, individuals should write directly to the school, institution, organization, or government agency concerned at least eight to ten months prior to the beginning of the academic year in the foreign country in which it is located. Included in initial correspondence should be any supportive materials that might be helpful: references, school transcripts, publications, and proof of teaching experience. The majority of institutions surveyed reported that a minimum of one year's teaching experience was at least preferred, if not required, of prospective faculty. Some institutions report a preference for between two and five years' experience.

After reviewing all documentation, a personal interview may be required. Overseas sponsors will often make seasonal trips to the United States specifically to recruit staff and conduct these interviews. In other instances, a U.S. agency may be hired to handle the interview process and issue a report to the overseas sponsor.

Salary and Other Benefits

It is extremely important that a teacher fully understand all the conditions and arrangements involved in any assignment before it is accepted. The following are some items that may need to be worked out to the teacher's and sponsor's mutual satisfaction before final acceptance of a job offer: salary, health and life insurance; educational opportunities for children; tax advantages; transportation to and from the United States for teacher and dependents; home leave and/or other vacation privileges; available housing; and the availability and cost of local medical services.

There is a wide variation in basic salary levels and other benefits offered to U.S. teachers abroad. One school might provide housing or a housing allowance in addition to salary, but not offer transportation. Another school might offer salary and free tuition for dependent children. An individual should not, however, expect that salary levels, food, living conditions, or benefits be similar to those in the United States.

GOVERNMENT REGULATIONS

Many foreign countries have strict laws regarding paid employment by foreign nationals. This is seen especially in times of economic hardship when competition for jobs may be very stiff among the country's citizenry and there is a fear that foreign nationals will assume positions that could be filled by local nationals. It is imperative, therefore, to investigate as soon as possible the regulations concerning work visas or permits in the country of interest.

Often, an individual must possess evidence that employment has been secured before a permit will be issued. Overseas sponsors may make all these arrangements. If not, one should contact the foreign embassy for the particulars of the laws and application procedures. A listing of foreign embassies and their addresses appears on pages 107–117.

Foreign governments also have their own immunization requirements. Current information is available from local or state health departments and foreign embassies or from the *World Immunization Risk Chart* (available from the International Association for Medical Assistance to Travelers, Suite 5620, Empire State Building, 350 Fifth Avenue, New York, NY 10001), which contains a list of the immunization requirements of countries worldwide. At the present time, travelers to Europe do not require any inoculations.

Passports and Visas.

Each U.S. citizen departing from the United States must, in most cases, carry a valid U.S. passport. Exceptions are made for travel to any U.S. territory, Canada, and most countries in Central and South America and the Caribbean. If foreign governments do not require a U.S. passport, they may require documentary evidence of U.S. citizenship. Those needing passports may apply for them at any passport office located in the following cities: Boston, Chicago, Honolulu, Houston, Los Angeles, Miami (Florida), New Orleans, New York City, Philadelphia, San Francisco, Seattle, Stamford (Connecticut) and Washington, D.C. Passports are also available from federal court clerks, clerks of any state court of record, judges or clerks of any probate court, and postal clerks designated by the Postmaster General.

Visa requirements and arrangements should be checked with the institution or organization abroad to which one is applying. Information on visa requirements may be obtained from foreign embassies in the United States or from the Department of State publication *Visa Requirements of Foreign Governments,* available in any passport office.

Taxes

Before departing from the United States, all the rules and regulations concerning the payment of U.S. income taxes while abroad should be investigated. Information may be obtained from any local IRS office. One IRS booklet that may be helpful is *Foreign Tax Credit for U.S. Citizens and Resident Aliens.*

HOW TO USE THIS BOOK

The descriptions of faculty needs and available opportunities for U.S. teachers abroad were derived from direct communication with officials from U.S. and foreign government agencies and private organizations and from American and international schools abroad, as listed in *Schools Abroad of Interest to Americans* (see Bibliography). Respondents were asked to describe, by questionnaire and supportive materials, faculty and educational needs and/or the scope of teacher exchange programs. In spite of repeated mailings, it is inevitable that some country or program information has been missed.

All entries are listed alphabetically by country within their broad geographical region of the world. Entries include the name and address of the responding organization, agency, or institution and offer brief but specific information on the country's or institution's academic calendar, language of instruction, and faculty needs and composition. For sponsoring organizations, general information is included on the scope of the exchange program and any restrictions.

The following general sections can be found in most entries:

Opportunities: This section lists availablity of positions according to level of instruction and subject areas.

Requirements: Academic and language prerequisites, including experience and certification requirements, are mentioned here. Restrictions (such as "teaching couples only" or a limited number of dependents provided for) are also noted. If requirements for teachers of English as a second/foreign language are different from those for teachers of other subjects, this information is provided separately.

Duration: Average length of contract and renewal options are noted.

Benefits: This section lists salary and stipends, including type of currency and extent of fringe benefits, such as transportation, housing, medical and other insurance, tuition for dependents, and vacation and home leave. If preassignment orientation is provided, entry describes its location and duration.

Application: Deadline for submission of application and supportive materials and notification date of acceptance are provided.

Contact: Address to which additional inquiries and requests for application materials should be directed is listed here.

The remainder of the book consists of the following:

Sources of Additional Information

This section describes organizations and agencies which do not sponsor formal teacher exchange programs but will provide information or publications to assist U.S. nationals seeking employment opportunities abroad.

Embassy Listing

Names and addresses of all foreign embassies located in the United States are provided here.

Foreign Currency

A list of foreign currency and the exchange-rate equivalency in U.S. dollars is included in this directory. Since these rates change daily, this listing is only meant to provide general information, and rates should be checked prior to departure from the United States.

Bibliography

This annotated bibliography describes publications that may assist U.S. nationals seeking teaching positions overseas. Many of the books provide information on travel, work, and study abroad, while others provide specific information on overseas schools and postsecondary institutions.

Note: The Institute of International Education is not in a position to endorse an agency or evaluate programs. Inclusion in this directory does not imply approval by the Institute, nor does an omission imply its disapproval.

WORLDWIDE

Center for Applied Linguistics,
3520 Prospect St., Washington, DC 20007.
   This U.S.-based organization founded in 1959 serves U.S., Southeast Asian, and Middle Eastern teachers, lecturers, TESL/TEFL, administrators, curriculum developers, guidance counselors, and researchers.
Opportunities: *Southeast Asia Regional Service Center.* Five to ten positions annually including two to three teachers of English as a second/foreign language positions. Much of the work is in technical assistance, curriculum design, and evaluation. Overseas positions are rarely for direct teaching activities.
Requirements: U.S. master's degree in applied linguistics or teaching English as a second/foreign language is required; U.S. Ph.D. degree in applied linguistics is preferred. Host country language proficiency on the intermediate or advanced level is preferred. Previous practical experience is required. Previous international experience is preferred.
Duration: One year; renewable for one year or to project completion.
Benefits: Salary varies. Three-day pre-assignment orientation in Washington, DC. Transportation is included. Housing allowance is included; full cost of housing is not always covered.
Application: Open.
Contact: MaryAnn Zima, Center for Applied Linguistics, 3520 Prospect St., Washington, DC 20007.

Council for International Exchange of Scholars (CIES),
11 Dupont Circle, Suite 300, Washington, DC 20036.
   Founded in 1947, CIES serves worldwide teachers, lecturers, TESL/TEFL, administrators, curriculum developers, guidance counselors, and researchers in all areas of senior scholarship and artistic professions through its administration of the *Fulbright-Hays Senior Scholar Program.*
Opportunities: *Fulbright-Hays Senior Scholar Program.* Grants for university teaching and advanced research. Most grants are for the academic year of the host institution or country — September/October to June/July — or for a period within the calendar year. Grants for a shorter period than an academic year are available in a number of countries. Multi-country or regional programs offer awards tenable in one or more countries.
Requirements: U.S. citizenship. Foreign language proficiency may be required. Advanced degree or professional qualifications are required. For lecturers these include postdoctoral college- or university-teaching experience at the level and in the subject field of the lectureship sought (including English as a second/foreign language). For researchers, these include a Ph.D. degree at the time of application or comparable professional qualifications.
Benefits: Roundtrip travel for lecturing grantee and one principal dependent is included when appointment is for an academic year, except in specified Western European countries. Maintenance allowance, generally paid in foreign currency, is provided to cover basic living costs for grantee and dependents. A monetary supplement for lecturers with assignments outside Western Europe is included. A small incidental allowance for travel, books, and services essential to the assignment is provided.
Application: CIES publishes *Awards Abroad*, an annual directory of specific grants, requirements, and deadlines.
Contact: Council for International Exchange of Scholars, 11 Dupont Circle, Suite 300, Washington, DC 20036.

Department of Defense Overseas Dependents Schools,
2461 Eisenhower Ave., Alexandria, VA 22331.
   Since 1946, elementary and secondary schools have been operating on U.S. military bases for the dependents of military and civilian personnel assigned abroad. The Department of Defense Overseas Dependents Schools include schools operated by the Army, Air Force, and Navy. There are about 270 such schools, with an enrollment of about 136,000 students and a staff of about 11,000 educational personnel, 99 percent of which is U.S. nationals.

Opportunities: Twenty countries worldwide. About 500 positions for teachers of general education on the primary level, all subjects on the secondary level, all areas of vocational/technical education, and special education specialists.

Requirements: U.S. bachelor's degree is required; U.S. master's degree is preferred. One year's previous teaching experience is preferred.

Duration: One to two years; renewable indefinitely.

Benefits: Salary is comparable with that of larger U.S. school districts. Preassignment orientation on major U.S. military bases. Transportation is included for appointee and dependents. Housing is included. Home leave is provided. Insurance and educational allowance for appointee and dependents are provided.

Application. January 15.

Contact: Teachers Recruitment Section, Department of Defense Overseas Dependents Schools, 2461 Eisenhower Ave., Alexandria, VA 22331.

European Council of International Schools (ECIS),

18 Lavant St., Petersfield, Hampshire GU32 3EW, England.

This U.S.- and foreign-based organization founded in 1965 serves teachers, administrators, guidance counselors, international schools, and parents. ECIS assists in staff recruitment by working with international schools and with individual members interested in posts at international schools. ECIS conducts an annual International Staff Recruitment Center each February in London.

ECIS publishes several books and materials, including *The Directory of International Schools*, a comprehensive, annual guide to international schools worldwide and the *International Schools Journal*, a semi-annual magazine of research. A mailing list subscription is $36 per year.

Opportunities: About 150 positions for teachers on the primary and secondary levels.

Requirements: U.S. bachelor's degree in appropriate field is required; U.S. master's degree is preferred. Foreign language proficiency can be useful. Two years' teaching experience is required. Previous international experience is preferred.

Duration: Two years; renewable depending upon country and school.

Benefits: Salary varies according to post, institution, and location. Transportation is included for appointee and dependents. Housing is sometimes included. Baggage allowance is provided. Tuition reduction for dependent children is available. Insurance coverage depends upon country's national programs.

Application: Spring for fall. Notification by May/June. Registrants agree to pay seven and one-half percent of first year's annual salary as placement fee.

Contact: Robert M. Sandoe and Associates, 29 Newbury St., Boston, MA 02116.

Institute of International Education (IIE),

809 United Nations Plaza, New York, NY 10017.

The Institute of International Education, founded in 1919, is the oldest and most active educational exchange agency in the United States. It administers educational programs on behalf of governments, foundations, corporations, universities, and international organizations.

Opportunities: *Register for International Service in Education (RISE)* is a computer-based referral service providing biographical data of individual registrants to prospective employers and overseas employment opportunities to individual registrants. The service to prospective employers enables universities, technical institutes, research centers, educational organizations, and government agencies abroad to locate possible candidates for employment. Individuals receive data on all overseas educational employment listed in the Register that correspond to the individual's qualifications and preferences.

IIE's only direct service to individual and institutional registrants is to supply the above information. It is the responsibility of both parties to explore mutual suitability for assignment and negotiate the contract terms. IIE cannot guarantee that employment will result.

The number and type of positions available in any given year vary and represent a broad range of disciplines and fields.

Requirements: Vary according to needs. Listed are general requirements. U.S. bachelor's degree is required; U.S. master's or Ph.D. degree is preferred. Two years' teaching experience is generally required. Foreign language proficiency is preferred. Previous international experience is preferred.

Benefits: Some positions offer salary and other benefits equivalent to or better than U.S. levels. Transportation, housing, home leave, and support for dependents may be included. In some developing countries, however, compensation may be lower than U.S. levels and faculty may be expected to pay their own living and travel expenses.

Application: Individuals pay $45 registration fee for one year.

Contact: Sandra Cervera, RISE, Institute of International Education (IIE), 809 United Nations Plaza, New York, NY 10017.

International School Services, Inc. (ISS),

P.O. Box 5910, Princeton, NJ 08540.

International Schools Service is a private, nonprofit organization founded in 1955 to support and advance the education of expatriate children living around the world. ISS services to overseas schools include recruitment and recommendation of personnel, curricular and administrative guidance, materials procurement, financial management, consulting services, publishing, and school management.

The American and international schools which utilize ISS recruitment services are overseas primary and secondary schools enrolling dependent children of business and diplomatic families. Generally, the language of instruction is English and curriculum is based on the U.S. model.

There are currently more than 700 schools affiliated with ISS located in Africa, Europe, Central and South America, the Middle East, and Asia. Most schools are independent and governed by a board of directors drawn from the communities served. Other are corporate-sponsored or affiliated with religious organizations.

Opportunities: *Educational Staffing.* About 200 positions for teachers, administrators, and guidance counselors on the primary and secondary levels in all subject areas, including English as a second/foreign language, special education, and speech therapy.

Requirements: U.S. bachelor's degree is required; U.S. master's degree is preferred. Two years' recent teaching experience is required; experience is waived for teachers of mathematics, science, physical education, and library science. Previous international experience is preferred by the recruiting schools.

For *TESL/TEFL:* U.S. bachelor's degree is required. Two year's teaching experience is required. Previous international experience is preferred.

Duration: Two years; renewable for one to two years.

Benefits: Salary is established by each recruiting school based on the cost of living. Pre-assignment orientation is the responsibility of each school. Transportation is included for appointee and varying number of dependents based on schools' established policies. Housing is provided. Dependent children generally receive free tuition. Individual school establishes other benefits including insurance, home leave, contract bonus, cost-of-living allowances, baggage and storage allowances, sick leave, and foreign service premium.

Application: One year in advance of desired recruitment. Fifty dollar registration and $600 placement fees are required. Depending on the school, location, and type of position, the school may pay a portion of the placement fee.

Contact: Educational Staffing, International Schools Services, Inc. (ISS), P.O. Box 5910, Princeton, NJ 08540.

National Science Foundation (NSF),

Division of International Programs, Washington, DC 20550.

The National Science Foundation Division of International Programs coordinates scientific exchange activities and maintains liaison with foreign agencies of the cooperating countries listed below.

Opportunities: *The U.S.-Eastern European Cooperative Science Programs.* These programs foster and support scientific cooperation between the United States and Bulgaria, Czechoslovakia, East Germany, Hungary, and Romania. They promote collaboration and exchange of information between scientists, engineers, and institutions of research and higher learning of the United States and the cooperating countries. The U.S.-Eastern European Cooperative Science Programs offer support for three types of activities: scientific visits, joint seminars/workshops, and cooperative research.

Requirements: American scientists eligible to participate in these programs include members of universities and colleges, professional societies, and other scientific institutions of the public and private sector. Participants must send preliminary proposal to the Foundation, along with a list of all other current research with which they are involved.

Benefits: Roundtrip transportation at the lowest available rate is included. Support for visitor's dependents will be provided at negotiated rates if the visit exceeds five months. Partial salary compensation, per diem allowance are provided.

Application: Four months prior (for scientific visits), twelve months prior for seminars or workshops, and nine months prior for cooperative research projects.

Contact: U.S.-Eastern European Cooperative Science Programs, National Science Foundation, Division of International Programs, Washington, DC 20550.

Northfield Mount Hermon School,
Northfield, MA 01360.

This U.S.-based secondary school maintains an ongoing exchange of students and teachers with the following institutions: Schutz America School (Alexandria, Egypt), America School (Tangiers, Morocco), Waterford Kamhlaba School (Mbabane, Swaziland), and the Woodstock School (Mourssoorie, India). In addition, U.S. teachers are employed in the term-abroad programs located in France, Spain, Morocco, and the Dominican Republic.

Opportunities: One position available in each country mentioned above during the academic year and one summer position each in France, Spain, and England (tentative).

Requirements: U.S. bachelor's is required; U.S. master's is preferred. French or Spanish language proficiency on the advanced level is required. Two years' teaching experience is required. Previous international experience is required.

Benefits: Salary is about $1,500, plus expenses for the summer. Transportation is included for appointee only. Housing is provided. Medical insurance is provided.

Application: Interview is required.

Contact: Director, International Programs, Northfield Mount Hermon School, Northfield, MA 01360.

Peace Corps,
806 Connecticut Ave. NW, Washington, DC 20526.

The Peace Corps was founded in 1961 to aid developing countries and to promote cross-cultural awareness and understanding. In the host country, Peace Corps volunteers work for a government department, agency, or organization, are supervised by host nationals, speak the native language, and are subject to local laws.

Opportunities: *Peace Corps Volunteer Program.* About 1,042 positions for teachers on the primary, secondary, vocational/technical (secondary and postsecondary), university, professional-education, and adult-education levels. Positions are also available for special-education specialists. Some fields represented include mathematics, science, industrial arts and vocational education, English as a second/foreign language, and business. Farming, city planning, gardening, and masonry are just a sampling of the more than 300 skilled labor categories also needed.

Often volunteers will be teaching native teachers in addition to students. They will be classroom teachers and teacher trainers.

Requirements: U.S. bachelor's degree in appropriate field is required; U.S. master's degree is required for most university-level positions. French or Spanish language proficiency is preferred depending upon the country of assignment. Previous teaching experience is preferred. Previous international experience is preferred.

For *TESL/TEFL:* U.S. bachelor's degree is required; U.S. master's degree in linguistics is required for university positions. Foreign language proficiency is preferred and may be required depending on the assignment. Previous teaching experience is preferred. Previous international experience is preferred.

Duration: Two years; may be renewable for two years.

Benefits: Monetary compensation includes living allowance for food, clothing, housing, utilities, vacation, transportation, and incidentals. Pre-assignment orientation for maximum 14 weeks in the United States and in host country. Volunteers and trainees receive $12,500 life insurace. Medical care is provided. A $175 readjustment allowance for each month of service is paid about six weeks after termination; one-third of this allowance is available prior to departure from host country.

Application: Open.

Contact: Peace Corps Recruitment, 806 Connecticut Ave. NW, Washington, DC 20526.

U.S. Department of Education,
Rm. 5673, ROB #3 Bldg., Washington, DC 20202.

A teacher exchange program is administered by the Teacher Exchange Section of the Office of International Education as part of the *Fulbright-Hays Program.* The Teacher Exchange Branch publishes an annual announcement of opportunities, conducts the national competition for the grants to be awarded, and recommends candidates to the Department of State and the Board of Foreign Scholarships for grants to teach or attend seminars abroad.

Opportunities: *Teacher Exchange Program.* A one-to-one teacher exchange for primary and secondary school teachers and administrators and college faculty with individuals in selected countries. Participating countries for 1984-85 include Canada, Denmark, France, Federal Republic of Germany, Italy (tentative), Switzerland, and the United Kingdom.

Requirements: U.S. citizenship. U.S. bachelor's degree is required. Current, full-time teaching or administrative employment plus three years' teaching experience is required. Evidence of good health is required.

Teaching couples may apply; however, suitable exchanges are limited. Preference will be given to those candidates who have not previously participated in this program, although a teacher may reapply three years after completion of first exchange.

Benefits: Teachers selected for exchange in Canada, France, Germany, Switzerland, Italy, and the United Kingdom receive salary from the home institution. For assignment in Denmark and the J.F. Kennedy School in Berlin, the U.S. teachers obtain an unpaid leave-of-absence and receive a maintenance allowance in the currency of the host country.

Duration: One academic year.

Application: October 15; notification by April.

Contact: Teacher Exchange Branch, U.S. Department of Education, Rm. 5673, ROB #3 Bldg., Washington, DC 20202.

Opportunities: *Seminars Abroad Program.* Enables secondary school teachers, administrators and curriculum specialists, and two- and four-year college instructors and professors to attend professional seminars abroad. Participating countries include Canada, People's Republic of China, India, Israel, Italy, Korea, Liberia, the Netherlands, and Pakistan.

Requirements: U.S. citizenship. U.S. bachelor's degree is required. Current, full-time employment in the subject area of the seminar is required. Two years' teaching experience is required; social studies supervisors and curriculum directors must have three years' teaching experience in and be professionally involved with the subject area of the seminar. Evidence of good health is required.

Preference will be given to applicants who have not previously participated in the program and who have not visited the country of application.

Dependents are not permitted to accompany seminar participants.

Benefits: The terms of award for seminars vary. Specific information is included in the Country Index for seminars in each participating country. Maintenance allowances, when provided, are paid in the currency of the host country.

Application: October 15; notification by April.

Contact: Teacher Exchange Branch, U.S. Department of Education, Rm. 5673, ROB #3 Bldg., Washington, DC 20202.

The United Nations Educational, Scientific and Cultural Organization (Unesco), with headquarters in Paris, provides technical assistance in education through projects located in many of the developing countries in Latin America, the Near East, South Asia, the Far East, and Africa. The Department of Education is responsible for seeking qualified U.S. citizens to refer to Unesco for its field positions.

Opportunities: *Unesco Technical Assistance Field Staff Program.* Highly experienced and specialized U.S. citizens may compete in an international selection process for a limited number of experts' posts in developing countries. The principal fields include teacher education; regional and national education planning; work-oriented functional literacy; educational research; physical sciences; engineering education; and technical, agricultural, and vocational training. In general, there are no opportunities for primary and secondary school personnel, except for a limited number in possession of highly technical skills.

Requirements: Proficiency in a foreign language is required. Five to ten years' associated experience at the Ph.D. level is generally required.

Application: The Division of International Services and Improvement will provide referral and general information services for applicants.

Contact: Division of International Services and Improvement, U.S. Department of Education, ROB #3, Seventh and D Sts. SW, Washington, DC 20202.

U.S. Information Agency, Washington, DC 20547.

The USIA *English Teaching Fellow Program* facilitates the recruitment of teachers of English as a foreign language and program administrators employed by binational commissions or similar autonomous institutions involved in English-teaching activities. USIA assembles dossiers of candidates which are sent to the hiring institution for review and selection. A successful candidate is an employee of the binational commission or institution, not of USIA. The program is administered primarily in Latin America, although there are occasional requests from institutions in Africa and Asia.

Opportunities: *English Teaching Fellow Program.* Eight to ten positions for teachers of English as a foreign language. Teaching fellows are full-time faculty. They may teach maximum 25 hours per week or be assigned to materials development or supervisory activities.

Requirements: U.S. bachelor's degree in applied linguistics or teaching English as a foreign language is required; U.S. master's degree in teaching English as a foreign language is preferred. Spanish language proficiency on the intermediate level is required. Previous teaching experience is not required; applicants must have completed student teaching.

Duration: One year; renewable for one year.

Benefits: Salary is $10,000 - $20,000 per year. Two-day pre-assignment orientation in Washington, DC. Transportation is included for candidate only. Housing is not included. Group policy medical insurance is available. Fellows receive any extra benefits or bonuses extended to local teachers. There is no provision for dependents; salary is considered sufficient to support only one person.

Application: Open. Starting dates vary according to country.

Contact: U.S. Information Agency, English Teaching Fellow Program, English Teaching Division (ECA/CE) Washington, DC 20547.

AFRICA, SOUTH OF THE SAHARA

MORE THAN ONE COUNTRY

TransCentury Corporation,
1789 Columbia Rd. NW, Washington, DC 20009.

In the past, the TransCentury Corporation placed a limited number of teachers, particularly within the fields of nonformal education and agriculture-related curriculum development, with the ministries and universities in Nigeria, Ethiopia, Botswana, and Lesotho in response to requests for specific positions under TransCentury's manpower development projects. The majority of the positions for which TransCentury recruits have been in agriculture, engineering, health, and management.

In recent years the focus is oriented more toward providing direct technical assistance in rural development, agriculture, and investment training.

TransCentury operates a Recruitment Center which maintains a talent bank of overseas professionals and produces the *Job Opportunities Bulletin,* which lists specific job openings and also contains a section in which individuals seeking development positions can announce their availability.

BURUNDI

American Cultural Center,
B.P. 810, 20-22 Chaussee Prince Louis Rwagasore, Bujumbura, Burundi.

Opportunities: *English Teaching Program.* One position annually for teachers of English as a foreign language or director of courses. American Culture Center acts as a placement agency.

Requirements: U.S. master's degree in TEFL is required. French language proficiency on the intermediate level is required. Previous teaching experience is preferred. Previous international experience is preferred.

Duration: One year; renewable.

Benefits: Salary is $25,000. Two-day pre-assignment orientation in Washington, DC. Transportation is included for appointee only. Housing is included only if candidate teaches at the University of Burundi. Appointees have use of Embassy pouch and health unit privileges.

Application: May.

Contact: USIA African Affairs Section (AF) or USIA English-Teaching Section (E/CE), U.S. Information Agency, Washington, DC 20547.

CAMEROON

Embassy of the United Republic of Cameroon,
2349 Massachusetts Ave. NW, Washington, DC 20008.

Academic calendar runs from September to July. Primary languages of instruction are French and English.

The Embassy reports a need for lecturers and guidance counselors for vocational/technical (secondary and postsecondary), university, and professional (e.g., teacher colleges) education.

There is no formal employment program for hiring U.S. educators. Listed is general information on faculty recruitment.

Requirements: U.S. bachelor's degree in mathematics, physics is preferred; U.S. master's degree in same or engineering is preferred; U.S. Ph.D. degree in same or agriculture is preferred. French language proficiency on the intermediate level is required. Previous teaching experience is preferred.

Duration: Two years; renewable.

Benefits: Salary is based upon qualifications. Transportation is not included. Housing is included. Technical allowance and rent allowance are provided.

Contact: The Cameroon Embassy, 2349 Massachusetts Ave. NW, Washington, DC 20008; Chancellor, University of Yaounde, P.O. Box 337, Yaounde, Cameroon; or Ministry of Labour, Yaounde, Cameroon.

CENTRAL AFRICAN REPUBLIC

American Embassy-American Cultural Center,
Bangui, Central African Republic.
   Academic calendar runs all year. Primary language of instruction is English; secondary language of instruction is French. The Embassy reports one small, self-supporting program for English language teachers on beginning, intermediate, and advanced levels.

ETHIOPIA

International Community School,
P.O. Box 70282, Addis Ababa, Ethiopia.
   This private, coed primary/secondary institution was founded in 1966. Academic calendar runs from September to June. Primary language of instruction is English; other languages of instruction are Amharic, French, German, Arabic, and Spanish. Current enrollment is 345; 25 percent of faculty are U.S. nationals.
Opportunities: Three to five positions annually for English, math and science teachers and one TESL/TEFL teacher on primary and secondary levels.
Requirements: U.S. bachelor's degree in subject area required. Two years' teaching experience is required. Previous international experience is preferred.
   For *TESL/TEFL:* U.S. bachelor's degree in applied linguistics is preferred. Two years' teaching experience is preferred. Previous international experience is preferred.
Duration: Two years; renewable indefinitely.
Benefits: Salary is 18,000–32,000 Ethiopian Birr. No pre-assignment orientation. Transportation is included for appointee and dependents. Housing is included. Home leave is included every two years. Free tuition for employees' dependents enrolled at school, Blue Cross/Blue Shield and Major Medical Plans are included; 100 Birr per month transportation allowance, 2,000–3,000 Birr per month settling-in allowance, 150 Kg. shipping allowance are provided.
Application: March.
Contact: Dr. J. R. Bowditch, International Community School, P.O. Box 70282, Addis Ababa, Ethiopia.

GABON

American International School of Libreville (AISL),
Dept. of State—Libreville, Washington, DC 20520.
This is a private, coed primary institution. Academic calendar runs from September to June. Primary language of instruction is English; secondary language of instruction is French. Current enrollment is 40; 30 percent of faculty are non-native; 66 percent of faculty are U.S. nationals.
Opportunities: Two positions available on K-8 levels.
Requirements: U.S. bachelor's degree in primary education is required; U.S. master's degree in primary education is preferred. French language proficiency on the intermediate level is preferred. Two to three years' teaching experience is required. Previous international experience is preferred.
Duration: Two years; renewable for two years.
Benefits: Salary is about $10,000, depending upon experience. No pre-assignment orientation. Transportation is included for appointee and dependents. Housing is included. Dependents under the age of 15 can attend the school. Blue Cross/ Blue Shield and Medevac insurance is provided.

Application: February.
Contact: Richard Spradling, Principal, AISL, Dept. of State—Libreville, Washington, DC 20520.

GHANA

Ghana Permanent Mission to the United Nations,
19 E. 47th St., New York, NY 10017.
Academic calendar runs from September to June/July. Primary language of instruction is English; secondary language of instruction is Akan.
The Permanent Mission to the U.N. reports a need for U.S. teachers and U.S. teachers of TESL/TEFL on secondary; vocational/technical (secondary), university, and professional levels. The government will assist in locating positions.
Requirements: French language proficiency is preferred. Previous teaching experience is required.
For *TESL/TEFL:* U.S. bachelor's degree in English literature is required; U.S. Ph.D. degree in linguistics/applied linguistics is required. French language proficiency on the intermediate level is preferred. Previous teaching experience is preferred. Previous international experience is preferred.
Duration: Two years; renewable for two years.
Benefits: Salary is negotiable, depending upon experience. Transportation is not included. Housing is included. Monetary educational allowances for dependents are included.
Contact: Ministry of Education, P.O. Box M. 45, Accra, Ghana.

GUINEA

Ministry of Higher Education,
P.O. Box 1003, Conakry, People's Revolutionary Republic of Guinea.
Academic calendar runs from October to July. Primary languages of instruction are the various national languages; secondary language of instruction is French; other language of instruction is English.
The Ministry reports that positions are only available through the auspices of cultural agreements made between the United States and Guinea (see CIES, Fulbright-Hays Program).

IVORY COAST

International School of Abidjan,
01 B.P. 1712, Abidjan, Ivory Coast.
This private, coed primary/secondary institution was founded in 1972. Academic calendar runs from September to June. Primary language of instruction is English; secondary language of instruction is French. Current enrollment is 265; 100 percent of faculty are non-native; 50 percent of faculty are U.S. nationals.
Opportunities: Four positions annually for all subjects on primary and secondary levels, including TESL.
Requirements: U.S. bachelor's degree in education is required.
For *TESL/TEFL:* U.S. bachelor's degree in English is preferred; U.S. master's degree in TESL is required. French language proficiency on the intermediate/advanced level is preferred. Two years' teaching experience is required. Previous international experience is preferred.
Duration: Two years; renewable for one or two years.
Benefits: Salary, payable in Central French African Francs, is based upon experience. No pre-assignment orientation. Transportation is included for appointee only. Housing is included for appointee and dependents.

Application: May.
Contact: The Director, International School of Abidjan, 01 B.P. 1712, Abidjan 0, Ivory Coast.

Ivory Coast Academy,
B.P. 1171, Bouake, Ivory Coast.
   This coed primary/secondary school for missionary children was founded in 1962. Academic calendar runs from September to July (three trimesters). Primary language of instruction is English; secondary language of instruction is French. Current enrollment is 165; 100 percent of faculty are U.S. nationals.
   There is no formal employment program for hiring U.S. educators. Listed is general information on faculty recruitment.
Opportunities: Positions for english, social studies, and math teachers for grades seven through 12.
Requirements: U.S. bachelor's degree in elementary education is required; U.S. master's degree in high school subject area is preferred. French language proficiency on the intermediate level is preferred. One year's teaching experience is required.
Duration: Two years.
Benefits: Teachers are under their own mission support. Pre-assignment orientation. Transportation is not included. Housing is included.
Contact: Ray Buker, Personnel Secretary, CBFMS, P.O. Box 5, Wheaton, IL 60189.

KENYA

Embassy of Kenya,
2249 R St. NW, Washington, DC 20008.
   Academic calendar runs from January to December. Primary language of instruction is English; other languages of instruction are vernacular languages and Swahili.
   The Embassy reports that there is a need for U.S. teachers. The U.S. Agency for International Development and the Peace Corps does recruitment based on Kenyan government needs.
Contact: Peace Corps, 806 Connecticut Ave. NW, Washington, DC 20525; U.S. Agency for International Development, Washington, DC 20523; or U.S. Embassy, Nairobi, Kenya.

International School of Kenya,
Box 14103, Nairobi, Kenya.
   This private, coed primary/secondary institution was founded in 1970. Academic calendar runs from August 15 to June 8. Primary language of instruction is English; other languages of instruction are French, Spanish, and German. Current enrollment is 600; 100 percent of faculty are non-native; 75 percent of faculty are U.S. nationals.
Opportunities: *ESL Elementary or High School.* Two to three positions available annually for TESL/TEFL teachers on primary and secondary levels.
Requirements: U.S. bachelor's degree in TESL/TEFL is required; U.S. master's degree in TESL/TEFL is preferred. Two years' teaching experience is preferred. Previous international experience is preferred.
Duration: At least two years; renewable indefinitely.
Benefits: Salary $14,000–$25,000, depending upon experience and education. Transportation is included. Housing allowance of $5,500–$6,900 per year depending on family is included. Educational opportunities are provided by University of South Carolina on school campus. Insurance is provided.
Application: December.
Contact: Brian McCauley, International School of Kenya, Box 14103, Nairobi, Kenya.

LESOTHO

Lesotho Mission to the United Nations,
866 U.N. Plaza, New York, NY 10017.

Academic calendar runs from January to December. Primary language of instruction is English; secondary language of instruction is Sesotho.

The Permanent Mission to the U.N. reports that U.S. mathematics and science teachers, educational administrators, and teachers of English as a second language are needed on all levels. The government assists in locating positions.

Contact: Permanent Secretary, Ministry of Education, Maseru, Lesotho.

Maseru English Medium Preparatory School,
P.O. Box 34, Maseru 100, Lesotho.

This public, coed primary institution was founded in 1890. Academic calendar runs from September to July. Primary language of instruction is English; other languages of instruction are French, Afrikaans, Sesotho. Current enrollment is 460.

Opportunities: Positions on primary level for general education.

Requirements: U.S. bachelor's degree in primary education is required. Three years' teaching experience is preferred.

Duration: Two to two-and-one-half years.

Benefits: Salary is 5,664–10,400 Maloti per year. Transportation is included for appointee and dependents. Housing is included. Cape Medical scheme, home insurance are included.

Application: March.

Contact: The Management Committee, Maseru English Medium Preparatory School, P.O. Box 34, Maseru 100, Lesotho.

LIBERIA

American Cooperative School,
c/o U.S. Embassy, P.O. Box 98, Monrovia, Liberia.

This private, coed primary/secondary institution was founded in 1960. Academic calendar runs from August to June. Primary language of instruction is English. Current enrollment is 400; 100 percent of faculty are non-native; 98 percent of faculty are U.S. nationals.

Opportunities: Four to eight positions annually for math, science, and business education on secondary level.

Requirements: U.S. bachelor's degree is required; U.S. master's degree is preferred. Two years' teaching experience is preferred. U.S. teacher certification is required.

Duration: Two years.

Benefits: Salary is $9,117–$13,787 per year, 64% nontaxable. Transportation is included for appointee and dependents. Housing is included for appointee and dependents; free tuition is available for dependents at ACS. Blue Cross/Blue Shield full payment, TIAAA/CREF 5% matched contribution are included.

Application: Varies with need.

Contact: Richard C. Chesley, Superintendent, American Cooperative School, c/o U.S. Embassy, P.O. Box 98, Monrovia, Liberia.

MADAGASCAR

Permanent Mission of Madagascar to the United Nations,
801 Second Ave., New York, NY 10017.

Academic calendar runs from September to June. Primary language of instruction is Malagasy; other languages of instruction are French and English.

The Permanent Mission to the U.N. reports no need for U.S. teachers or educational administrators. U.S. teachers are recruited and employed by the U.S. Cultural Center in Antananarivo, the capital city, for language teaching. Conditions of recruitment and employment are set by the U.S. Government. As far as the government of Madagascar is concerned, in general, it prefers to recruit foreign technical staff, including teachers, through bilateral agreement.

MALI

Ministry of Education,
Ghazee Building, 20-05 Male', Republic of Maldives.
Academic calendar runs from February to December. Primary language of instruction is Dhivehi; secondary language of instruction is English.
The Ministry reports that there is a need for U.S. teachers, educational administrators, and teachers of English as a second/foreign language.
Opportunities: Positions annually on primary, secondary, vocational/technical and professional levels.
Requirements: U.S. bachelor's degree is required; U.S. master's degree is preferred. Three years' teaching experience is required. Previous international experience is preferred.
For *TESL/TEFL:* U.S. bachelor's degree in linguistics is required. Three years' teaching experience is required. Previous international experience is preferred.
Duration: Three years; renewable.
Benefits: Transportation is not included. Housing is included for appointee and dependents. Home leave is included. Educational opportunities/monetary educational allowances for dependents are provided. Medical expenses are paid.
Application: August; notification before end of year.
Contact: Ministry of Education, Ghazee Building, 20-05 Male', Republic of Maldives.

MAURITIUS

Embassy of Mauritius,
Suite 134, Van Ness Centre, 4301 Connecticut Ave. NW, Washington, DC 20008.

Ministry of Education and Cultural Affairs,
Government Centre, Port Louis, Mauritius.
Academic calendar runs from January to November. Primary language of instruction is English; secondary language of instruction is French.
The Ministry and Embassy report that there is no need for U.S. teachers, educational administrators, or teachers of English as a second/foreign language at this time.

NIGERIA

Embassy of Nigeria,
2201 M St. NW, Washington, DC 20037.
Academic calendar runs from September to June. Primary language of instruction is English.
The Embassy reports a need for U.S. teachers, lecturers, curriculum developers, researchers, and teachers of English as a second/foreign language on all educational levels. Listed is general information about faculty recruitment.
Requirements: U.S. bachelor's or master's degree in the humanities or sciences is required; U.S. Ph.D. degree is required for positions in postsecondary institutions and universities. Previous teaching experience is required.
For *TESL/TEFL:* U.S. bachelor's degree in linguistics, applied linguistics, or English is required; U.S. master's or Ph.D. degree is preferred. Previous teaching experience is preferred.
Duration: Two years; renewable for two years.
Benefits: Transportation is included for appointee, spouse, and four dependents. Housing is included. Home leave is included. Medical insurance is provided.
Contact: Federal Ministry of Education, PMB 12573, Lagos, Nigeria.

SOUTH AFRICA

U.S. Information Service,
Second Floor, Scott's Building, 10 Plein St., Cape Town, South Africa.

The USIS Office reports that because of South Africa's labor laws, it is difficult for foreigners to obtain work permits. The law states that permits will be issued only if there are no South Africans available to fill the positions.

As a result, some U.S. nationals have been invited to teach at South African universities for varying lengths of time in fields where expertise is not available among South African citizens. Direct contact with individual universities may result in such employment.

SWAZILAND

Swaziland College of Technology,
P.O. Box 69, Mbabane, Swaziland.

This public, coed vocational/technical (postsecondary) institution was founded in 1968. Academic calendar runs from January to December. Primary language of instruction is English. Current enrollment is 570; 10 percent of faculty are non-native; at present there is no U.S. faculty.

Opportunities: Two to four positions annually.

Requirements: U.S. bachelor's or master's degree in engineering is preferred. Two years' teaching experience is preferred; work experience in relevant technical field is required. Previous international experience is preferred.

For *TESL/TEFL:* U.S. bachelor's degree in English for technical or business is required. Three years' teaching experience is required. Previous international experience is preferred.

Duration: Thirty months; renewable for 30 months.

Benefits: All assignments are voluntary. Transportation is not included. Housing is included. Medical care is provided.

Application: No deadline; notification within one month.

Contact Principal, Swaziland College of Technology, P.O. Box 69, Mbabane, Swaziland.

TOGO

American International School of Lome,
c/o American Embassy Lome, Dept. of State, Washington, DC 20520.

This private, coed primary level institution was founded in 1966. Academic calendar runs from September to June. Primary language of instruction is English; secondary language of instruction is French. Current enrollment is 74; 50 percent of faculty are non-native; 41 percent of faculty are U.S. nationals.

There is no formal employment program for hiring U.S. educators. Listed is general information on faculty recruitment.

Opportunities: Positions for kindergarten teachers, teachers of grade levels one through eight, and library personnel. Most faculty members are recruited locally.

Requirements: U.S. bachelor's degree in education is required; U.S. master's degree is preferred; teaching certification is required. Two years' teaching experience is required.

Duration: Two years; renewable.

Benefits: Salary is 2.574.120–4.149.079 Central French African francs; up to 25 percent payable in U.S. dollars. Transportation is included for appointee and dependents. Housing allowance is included. Tuition assistance for dependent children is available. Medical insurance, one month's salary for relocation are provided.

Application: February; notification by April.

Contact: Principal, American International School of Lome, c/o American Embassy Lome, Dept. of State, Washington, DC 20520.

UGANDA

Embassy of the Republic of Uganda,
5909 16 St. NW, Washignton, DC 20011.

Academic calendar runs from June to March. Primary language of instruction is English; other languages of instruction are Luganda, Ateso, Lunyankole, and Lunyoro.

The Embassy reports a need for U.S. teachers and educational administrators for all educational levels. There is expressed need for science teachers. Listed is general information on faculty recruitment.

Requirements: U.S. bachelor's degree in sciences is required; U.S. master's degree is preferred; U.S. Ph.D. degree in sciences for university teaching is required. Previous teaching experience is preferred. Previous international experience is preferred.

Duration: Two to three years.

Benefits: Transportation is included for appointee and dependents. Housing is included.

Contact: Permanent Secretary, Ministry of Education, P.O. Box 7063, Kampala, Uganda.

UPPER VOLTA

Ministerè de l'Education Nationale des Arts et de la Culture,
B.P. 1308, Ougadougou, Upper Volta.

Ministry of Higher Education and Scientific Research,
University of Ougadougou, B.P. 7021, Upper Volta.

Embassy of the Republic of Upper Volta,
2340 Massachusetts Ave. NW, Washington, DC 20008.

Academic calendar runs from October to July. Primary language of instruction is French; other languages of instruction are English, German, and Spanish.

The Ministry and Embassy report a need for U.S. teachers, administrators, curriculum developers and teachers of English as a second/foreign language primarily on the university and other postsecondary levels. There is some expressed need for faculty for secondary education.

Listed is general information on faculty recruitment. In addition, teachers are recruited through the Peace Corps Program.

Requirements: U.S. Ph.D. degree preferred. French language proficiency on the intermediate level is preferred. Previous teaching experience is required. Previous international experience is preferred.

For *TESL/TEFL:* U.S. bachelor's or master's degree in applied linguistics or English is required; U.S. Ph.D. degree is preferred. French language proficiency on the intermediate level is preferred. Previous teaching experience is required. Previous international experience is preferred.

Duration: One to two years; renewable.

Benefits: Housing is included. Medical care is provided.

Application: May 15.

Contact: Embassy of the Republic of Upper Volta, 2340 Massachusetts Ave. NW, Washington, DC 20008; Permanent Mission of the Republic of Upper Volta to the United Nations, 866 U.N. Plaza, New York, NY 10017; Ministry of Higher Education and Scientific Research, University of Ougadougou, B.P. 7021, Upper Volta; or Ministerè de l'Education Nationale des Arts et de la Culture, B.P. 1308, Ougadougou, Upper Volta.

ZAIRE

American School of Kinshasa,
B.P. 4702, Kinshasa II, Zaire.

This private, coed primary/secondary institution was founded in 1962. Academic calendar runs from September to June. Primary language of instruction is English.

Current enrollment is 520; 98 percent of faculty are non-native; 80 percent of faculty are U.S. nationals. Students may represent up to 40 languages.

Opportunities: *Intercom.* About 10 positions annually. One teacher of English as a second/foreign language is needed about every three years. Teachers must be flexible; materials and services may not be on a par with those in the U.S.

Requirements: U.S. bachelor's degree is required; U.S. master's degree is preferred. French language proficiency on the intermediate level is preferred. Two years' teaching experience is preferred. Previous international experience is required. Teaching certification is required.

For *TESL/TEFL:* U.S. bachelor's or master's degree in linguistics, applied linguistics, or English is preferred. French language proficiency on the intermediate level is preferred. Previous teaching experience is preferred. Previous international experience is preferred. Experience with non-English speakers is preferred.

Duration: Three years; renewable.

Benefits: Salary is $14,098–$26,786, based upon experience and degree. Pre-assignment orientation via mail. Transportation is included for appointee and dependents. Housing is included. Home leave is included. Free tuition for dependent children is available. Life and medical insurance (with deductible), professional growth allowance are provided.

Application: January.

Contact: Superintendent, American School of Kinshasa, APO, NY 09662.

ZAMBIA

Ministry of General Education and Culture,
P.O. Box 50093, Lusaka, Zambia.

Academic calendar runs from January to December. Primary language of instruction is English; other languages of instruction are Cibemba, Nyanja, Tonga, Kaonde, Lozi, Lunda, and Lumale.

The Ministry reports that U.S. teachers are primarily recruited by and for Mission secondary schools.

International School of Lusaka,
P.O. Box 5021, Lusaka, Zambia.

This private, coed primary/secondary institution was founded in 1968. Current enrollment is 1,450 representing over 50 countries and languages. Faculty includes two full-time administrators, 39 full-time teachers with an average of ten years' experience, and support staff.

Opportunities: Eight to ten positions annually including one position for a teacher of English as a second language.

Requirements: U.S. bachelor's degree is required; U.S. master's or Ph.D. degree is preferred. Previous teaching experience is required. Previous international experience is preferred.

For *TESL/TEFL:* U.S. bachelor's degree in linguistics is preferred. Foreign language proficiency on the advanced level is required. Previous teaching experience is preferred. Previous international experience is preferred.

Duration: Four years; renewable for two years. For TESL: three years; renewable for two years.

Benefits: Salary is based upon degree and experience. Three-day pre-assignment orientation at school. Transportation is included for appointee and dependents. Housing is included. Free tuition for dependent children is available. Medical and life insurance is provided. Allowance of $3,500 is included.

Application: December for following September; notification by March.

Contact: Superintendent, International School of Lusaka, P.O. Box 5021, Lusaka, Zambia.

ZIMBABWE

Ministry of Education and Culture,
Box 8022, Causeway, Harare, Zimbabwe.

Academic calendar runs from January to December. Primary language of instruction is English.

The Ministry reports that there is no need for U.S. teachers or teachers of English as a second/foreign language at the present time.

MIDDLE EAST
AND NORTH
AFRICA

ALGERIA

Ministry of Education and Scientific Research,
1, rue Bachir Attar-Belcourt, Algiers, Algeria.

Academic calendar runs from September to June. Primary language of instruction is Arabic; secondary language of instruction is French; other language of instruction is English.

The Ministry reports that there is a need for U.S. teachers and lecturers on the university level and for teachers of English as a second/foreign language.

Opportunities: Positions for university professors, lecturers, and readers. About 20 positions available for teachers of English as a second/foreign language.

Requirements: U.S. Ph.D. degree in technology, sciences, mathematics, or literature is required. French language proficiency on the intermediate level is preferred. Previous teaching experience is preferred.

For *TESL/TEFL:* U.S. bachelor's degree in linguistics or English is required; U.S. master's degree in same or related fields of research is required; U.S. Ph.D. degree is preferred. French language proficiency on the intermediate level is preferred.

Duration: Two years; renewable.

Benefits: Salary is based upon education, experience, and rank. Transportation is included for appointee and dependents. Housing is not included. Medical insurance is provided.

Application: May/June.

Contact: Ministry of Education and Scientific Research, 1, rue Bachir Attar-Belcourt, Algiers, Algeria, or Embassy of the Democratic and Popular Republic of Algeria, Washington, DC.

American School of Algiers,
American Embassy, B.P. 549, Algiers, Algeria.

This private, coed primary institution was founded in 1964. Academic calendar runs from September to June. Primary language of instruction is English; secondary language of instruction is French. Current enrollment is 140; 75 percent of faculty are U.S. nationals.

Opportunities: Three to four positions annually for math/science teachers on primary level.

Requirements: U.S. bachelor's degree in elementary education is required; U.S. master's degree in elementary education is preferred. Three years' teaching experience is required. Previous international experience is preferred.

Duration: Two years; renewable for two years.

Benefits: Salary is $18,000–27,000. Transportation is included for appointee and dependent. Housing is included. Home leave, educational opportunities for dependents, and Blue Cross/Blue Shield major medical plans are also included as compensation.

Contact: Director, American School of Algiers, Dept. of State Algiers, Washington, DC 20520.

CYPRUS

Ministry of Education,
Nicosia, Cyprus.

Academic calendar runs from September to June. Primary language of instruction is Greek; other languages of instruction are English and French.

The Ministry reports no need for U.S. teachers. Opportunities for teachers can be found through the Fulbright-Hays Program.

TASIS Cyprus American School,
11 Kassos St., P.O. Box 2329, Nicosia, Cyprus.

This private, coed secondary institution was founded in 1979. Academic calendar runs from September to June. Primary language of instruction is English. Current enrollment is 160; 75 percent of faculty are non-native; 70 percent of faculty are U.S. nationals.

There is no formal employment program for hiring U.S. educators. Listed is general information on faculty recruitment.
Opportunities: Five positions annually for math and science teachers on secondary level.
Requirements: U.S. bachelor's degree in any discipline is required; U.S. master's degree in any discipline is preferred. Previous teaching experience is preferred. Previous international experience is preferred.
Duration: Two years; renewable indefinitely.
Benefits: Salary is $8,500–$12,000. One-week pre-assignment orientation in Cyprus. Housing is included. Travel allowance of $500, free tuition in school for dependents, standard medical insurance are included.
Application: January for September employment.
Contact: Dr. L. Ruth Clay, TASIS Cyprus American School, 11 Kassos St., P.O. Box 2329, Nicosia, Cyprus.

EGYPT

American University in Cairo,
113 Kasr-el-Aini St., Cairo, Egypt.
This private, coed university also offering adult education was founded in 1920. Academic calendar runs from mid-September to mid-June. Primary language of instruction is English. Current enrollment is 2,300 in degree programs, 9,500 in adult education programs; 50 percent of faculty are non-native; 45 percent of faculty are U.S. nationals.
There is no formal employment program for hiring U.S. educators. Listed is general information on faculty recruitment.
Opportunities: About 15 positions annually for engineering, computer science, economics, applied linguistics, and mass communications on the university level. About four teachers of English as a second/foreign language needed.
Requirements: U.S. Ph.D. degree in appropriate field is required. Two years' teaching experience is required. Previous international experience is preferred.
For *TESL/TEFL:* U.S. master's degree in teaching English as a foreign language is required. Any foreign language proficiency on the intermediate level is preferred. Two years' teaching experience is required. Previous international experience is preferred.
Duration: Two years; renewable.
Benefits: Salary is $12,300–$19,250; for TESL/TEFL, $8,950: paid in Egyptian and U.S. currency. One-week pre-assignment orientation on campus. Transportation is included for appointee and dependents. Housing is included. Paid tuition beyond $90 for dependent children and free tuition at university, home leave after two years are provided. Contribution schedule for group medical insurance and TIAA/CREF are included.
Application: December 31; notification by April/May.
Contact: Assistant to the Dean of the Faculty, American University in Cairo, 866 U.N. Plaza, New York, NY 10017.

Center for Arabic Study Abroad (CASA),
University of Washington, DH-20, Seattle, WA 98195.
This U.S.-based organization founded in 1967 serves American teachers and students with fellowships awarded for Arabic study in Cairo.
Opportunities: One position every two to four years.
Requirements: U.S. bachelor's degree in Arabic is required; U.S. master's degree in Middle Eastern Studies is preferred. Arabic language proficiency on the advanced level is required. Previous teaching experience is preferred. Previous international experience is preferred.
Duration: Two years.
Benefits: Salary depends upon experience. Transportation is included for appointee only. Housing is not included; sponsor will assist in locating housing. Home leave is included.
Contact: Center for Arabic Study Abroad (CASA), University of Washington, DH-20, Seattle, WA 98195.

Schutz American School,
P.O. Box 1000, Alexandria, Egypt.
This private, coed primary/secondary institution was founded in 1924. Academic calendar runs from September to June. Primary language of instruction is English. Current enrollment is 220; 70 percent of faculty are non-native; 65 percent of faculty are U.S. nationals.
There is no formal employment program for hiring U.S. educators. Listed is general information on faculty recruitment.
Opportunities: Five to ten positions annually for U.S. curriculum elementary/secondary education.
Requirements: U.S. bachelor's degree in appropriate field is required. Previous teaching experience is required. Previous international experience is preferred.
Duration: One year; renewable annually.
Benefits: Salary is $5,000–$10,000 plus room, board, and travel. One-week pre-assignment orientation at school. Transportation is included for appointee only. Housing is included. Free tuition for dependent children is included. TIAA and major medical are provided.
Application: No deadline.
Contact: Headmaster, Schutz American School, Box 27, FPO NY 09527.

ISRAEL

Ministry of Education and Culture,
34 Shivtei Yisrael, Jerusalem, Israel.

Embassy of Israel,
3514 International Dr. NW, Washington, DC 20008.
Academic calendar runs from September to June. Primary language of instruction is Hebrew; secondary language of instruction is Arabic.
The Ministry and Embassy report that there is no need for U.S. teachers, educational administrators, or teachers of English as a second/foreign language at the present time.

American International School in Israel,
Kfar Shmaryahu, Israel.
This private, coed primary/secondary institution, with facilities for special education, was founded in 1957. Academic calendar runs from September to June. Primary language of instruction is English. Current enrollment is 360; 80 percent of faculty are non-native; 70 percent of faculty are U.S. nationals.
Opportunities: Ten to 15 positions including one or two positions for teachers of English as a second/foreign language.
Requirements: U.S. bachelor's degree in elementary education is required; U.S. master's degree in education is preferred. No foreign language proficiency is required. Two years' teaching experience is required. Previous international experience is preferred.
For *TESL/TEFL:* U.S. master's degree in TEFL is preferred. Two years' teaching experience is required. Previous international experience is preferred.
Duration: Two years; renewable.
Benefits: Salary is paid in Israeli currency. One-week pre-assignment orientation. Transportation is included for appointee and dependents. Housing allowance is included; approximate cost of housing is $300–$500 per month.
Application: February 15; notification by April.
Contact: American International School in Israel, Kfar Shmaryaha, Israel.

KUWAIT

American School,
P.O. Box 6735, Hawalli, Kuwait.
This is a private, coed primary/secondary institution. Academic calendar runs from September to June. Primary language of instruction is English; secondary languages of

instruction are Arabic and French. Current enrollment is 1,050; 100 percent of faculty are non-native; 80 percent of faculty are U.S. nationals.
Opportunities: About 35 positions annually. Recruitment is conducted in the United States, Italy, France, Greece, and the United Kingdom.
Requirements: U.S. bachelor's degree is required; U.S. master's degree is preferred. Previous teaching experience is required. Previous international experience is preferred.
    For *TESL/TEFL:* U.S. bachelor's degree in English, linguistics, or applied linguistics is required; U.S. master's degree is preferred. Previous teaching experience is required. Previous international experience is preferred.
Duration: Two years; renewable annually.
Benefits: Salary is $13,793–$17,380 annually. One-week pre-assignment orientation. Transportation is included for appointee and dependents. Housing is included. Free tuition for dependent children, medical insurance are provided. Home leave after two years is included.
Application: May 1 for following year.
Contact: Superintendent, The American School, P.O. Box 6735, Hawalli, Kuwait.

MOROCCO

American Language Center,
1, Place de la Fraternité, Casablanca, Morocco.
    This foreign-based organization founded in the late 1950's serves African teachers, TESL/TEFL, administrators, curriculum developers, guidance counselors, and library faculty.
Opportunities: Four to five positions annually for teachers of English as a second/foreign language on all levels.
Requirements: U.S. bachelor's degree is required; U.S. master's degree in linguistics, applied linguistics, English literature, anthropology, sociology, or related fields is preferred. One to two years' teaching experience is preferred.
Duration: Two years; renewable for one year.
Benefits: Salary is 32–60 dirhams per hour depending upon experience and degree. Two-day pre-assignment orientation in Morocco. Transportation is not included. Housing is not included; approximate cost of housing is 800–1,500 dirhams per month. Eighty percent of all medical care is provided. Retirement plan is also available.
Application: April for academic year beginning in November; notification by June.
Contact: Director, American Language Center, 1, Place de la Fraternité, Casablanca, Morocco.

Rabat American School,
c/o American Embassy, Rabat, APO NY 09284.
    This private, coed primary/secondary institution was founded in 1962. Academic calendar runs from September to June. Primary language of instruction is English; other languages of instruction are French and Arabic. Current enrollment is 220; 95 percent of faculty are non-native; 88 percent of faculty are U.S. nationals.
    There is no formal employment program for hiring U.S. educators. Listed is general information on faculty recruitment.
Opportunities: One position annually for teacher of English as a second/foreign language on primary and secondary levels. In addition, teachers are needed for reading and language arts on primary level; in English and history on secondary level; special need for teachers of the learning disabled.
Requirements: U.S. bachelor's degree is required; U.S. master's degree in math, English, science, or history is preferred. French language proficiency is preferred. Two years' previous international teaching experience is required.
    For *TESL/TEFL:* U.S. bachelor's degree in applied linguistics is required; U.S. master's degree in applied linguistics is preferred. French language proficiency on the beginning level is preferred. Two years' teaching experience is required. Previous international experience is preferred.
Duration: One to two years; renewable for one to two years.

Benefits: Salary is $13,000–$19,000. Transportation is included for appointees and up to two dependents. Housing assistance is provided for appointees and dependents; approximate cost of housing is 1,500–2,500 Dhm per month. Home leave is included. Tuition discount for dependents, Blue Cross/Blue Shield medical insurance is provided.
Application: January 25; notification by cable or telephone.
Contact: Director, Rabat American School, c/o American Embassy, Rabat, APO NY 09284.

OMAN

U.S. Information Service,
P.O. Box 966, Muscat, Oman.
   The USIS Office reports a need for U.S. teachers of English as a second/foreign language on the primary, secondary, vocational/technical (secondary) levels and for professional educators in teacher-training colleges.
Requirements: U.S. bachelor's or master's degree in English or teaching English as a foreign language required; U.S. Ph.D. degree in teaching English as a foreign language is preferred. Arabic language proficiency on the intermediate level is preferred. Two years' teaching experience is required. Previous international experience is preferred.
Duration: Two years; renewable.
Benefits: Transportation is included. Housing is included.
Contact: Director, English Language Teaching Unit, P.O. Box 3, Muscat, Oman.

Sultan's School,
P.O. Box 9665, Seeb, Oman.
   This private, coed primary/secondary institution was founded in 1977. Academic calendar runs from September to May. Primary language of instruction is Arabic; other languages of instruction are English and French. Current enrollment is 380; 100 percent of faculty are non-native; 15 percent of faculty are U.S. nationals.
Opportunities: Four to six positions available for teachers of kindergarten and English, mathematics, science, and physical education on the secondary level. One to two positions for teachers of English as a second/foreign language available.
Requirements: U.S. bachelor's degree is required; U.S. master's degree is preferred. Arabic language proficiency on the beginning level is preferred. Three years' teaching experience is requried, preferably in the Middle East. Previous international experience is required.
   For *TESL/TEFL:* U.S. bachelor's or master's degree in linguistics, applied linguistics, or English is preferred. Arabic language proficiency on the beginning level is preferred. Three years' teaching experience is required. Previous international experience is required.
Duration: Two years; renewable.
Benefits: Salary is $17,000 per year paid in Oman rials. Three-day pre-assignment orientation in Oman. Transportation is included for appointee only. Housing is included. Seventy-five percent of tuition is paid for dependent children. Home leave is included. Full medical insurance is provided. A bonus of one month's salary is paid for every 12 months. Use of school's automotive vehicles, free utilities and services are provided.
Application: Open; preferably March for September.
Contact: The Headmaster, The Sultan's School, P.O. Box 9665, Seeb, Oman.

SAUDI ARABIA

Aramco Schools,
Box 73, Dhahran, Saudi Arabia.
   This private, coed primary-level institution encompassing grades kindergarten through nine was founded in 1945. Academic calendar runs from September to August.

Primary language of instruction is English. Current enrollment is 3,753; 90 percent of faculty are U.S. nationals.

There are nine Aramco schools located in four communities. Due to decreased oil production and subsequent budget cuts, no teaching positions will be available in 1984.

Listed is general information on faculty recruitment.

Opportunities: *TESOL.* Positions when available are for teachers of English as a second language on the primary level.

Requirements: U.S. bachelor's degree in linguistics is required. Three years' teaching experience is required.

Duration: No set contract.

Benefits: Salary is based upon degree and experience. One-week pre-assignment orientation in Houston at Aramco Services Co. Transportation is included for appointee and dependents. Housing may be included. Home leave is included annually. Continuing education opportunities are available. Life insurance and free medical care are provided.

Contact: Foreign Service Employment, Aramco Services Co., 1100 Milam, Houston, TX 77002.

Saudi Arabian International School—Dhahran District,

American Consulate General, APO NY 09616.

This private, coed primary/junior high school-level institution was founded in 1961. Academic calendar runs from September to June. Primary language of instruction is English. Current enrollment is 3,800; 100 percent of faculty are non-native; 96 percent of faculty are U.S. nationals.

Opportunities: Twenty to 80 teachers needed for self-contained classes, reading, music, art, and physical education on the primary level and social studies, mathematics, language arts, music, physical education and art on the junior high school level.

Requirements: U.S. bachelor's degree in appropriate field is required; U.S. master's degree in appropriate field is preferred. Two years' teaching experience is preferred.

For *TESL/TEFL:* U.S. bachelor's degree in linguistics is preferred. Two years' teaching experience is preferred.

Duration: Two years; renewable for two years maximum.

Benefits: Salary is $15,000–$32,000 based upon qualifications and experience. Transportation is included for appointee and dependents. Housing is included. Home leave is included. Tuition assistance for dependent children, major medical insurance are provided.

Application: January; notification by April.

Contact: Associate Superintendent, Personnel, Saudi Arabian International School—Dhahran District, American Consulate General, APO NY 09616.

SYRIA

Damascus Community School,

c/o American Embassy, Damascus, Syria.

This private, coed, primary-level (through grade nine) institution was founded in 1950. Academic calendar runs from September to June. Primary language of instruction is English; secondary languages of instruction are French and Arabic. Current enrollment is 250; 75 percent of faculty are non-native; 63 percent of faculty are U.S. nationals.

Opportunities: Five positions for administrators and teachers of language arts, science, social studies, and physical education for grades six through nine.

Requirements: U.S. bachelor's degree in appropriate field is required; U.S. master's degree is preferred. Two years' teaching experience is preferred.

Duration: Two years; renewable.

Benefits: Salary is $11,835–$17,185 per year. Transportation is included for appointee and dependents. Housing is included. Free tuition for dependent children, Blue Cross/Blue Shield for appointee and dependents are provided.

Application: January 1.

Contact: Principal, Damascus Community School, c/o Dept. of State, Washington, DC 20520.

TUNISIA

American Cooperative School of Tunis,
c/o U.S. Embassy, Tunis, Tunisia.

This is a private, coed primary-level (through grade nine) institution. Academic calendar runs from September to June. Primary language of instruction is English; secondary language of instruction is French. Current enrollment is 140; 80 percent of faculty are U.S. nationals.

Opportunities: Positions available for science and mathematics teachers for grades six through nine.

Requirements: U.S. bachelor's degree in appropriate field is required; U.S. master's degree is preferred. French language proficiency on the beginning or intermediate level is preferred. Two years' teaching experience is preferred. Previous international experience is preferred.

For *TESL/TEFL:* U.S. bachelor's degree in linguistics or English is preferred. French language proficiency is preferred. Two years' teaching experience is preferred.

Duration: Two years; renewable.

Benefits: Salary is based upon degree and experience. Five-day pre-assignment orientation on-site. Transportation is included for appointee and dependents. Housing is included. Home leave is included. Blue Cross/Blue Shield is provided.

Application: February 1; notification by April/May.

Contact: Director, American Cooperative School of Tunis, Dept. of State, Washington, DC 20520.

Bourguiba Institute of Modern Languages,
47, Avenue de la Liberte, Tunis, Tunisia 1002.

This public, coed university and adult education institution was founded in 1963. Academic calendar runs from October to June. Primary languages of instruction are French and Arabic for general subjects; other languages for language instruction include English, German, Italian, Russian, Spanish, Japanese, and Chinese. Current enrollment is 4,000; 45 to 50 percent of faculty are non-native; eight to 10 percent of faculty are U.S. nationals.

Opportunities: Positions for teachers of English as a foreign language.

Requirements: U.S. master's degree in English or linguistics is required; U.S. Ph.D. degree is preferred. French or Arabic language proficiency is preferred. Previous teaching experience is preferred. Previous international experience is preferred.

Duration: Two years; renewable.

Benefits: Salary varies according to degree. Transportation is included for appointee and dependents. Housing is not included; approximate cost of housing is 100–150 Tunisian Dinars per month. Medical insurance is provided.

Application: January/February.

Contact: Tunisian National Ministry of Higher Education or Bourguiba Institute of Modern Languages, 47, Avenue de la Liberte, Tunis, Tunisia 1002.

TURKEY

International Community School,
Robert College, P.K. 1, Istanbul, Turkey.

This private, coed primary institution encompassing grades kindergarten through nine was founded in 1911. Academic calendar runs from September to June. Primary language of instruction is English; other languages of instruction are French, Turkish, and Latin. Current enrollment is 177; 90 percent of faculty are U.S. nationals.

Opportunities: One position for a teacher of English as a foreign language.

Requirements: U.S. master's degree in teaching English as a foreign language or applied linguistics is required. Two years' teaching experience is preferred. Previous international experience is preferred.

Duration: Two years; renewable.

Benefits: Salary is $10,000 per year. Transportation is included for appointee and dependents. Housing is included. Life and health insurance is provided. Home leave is included. Monies to attend professional conferences are provided.
Application: No deadline.
Contact: International Community School, Robert College, P.K. 1, Istanbul, Turkey.

Robert College of Istanbul,
P.K. 1, Arnavutkoy, Istanbul, Turkey.
This is a private, coed secondary-level institution. Academic calendar runs from mid-September to mid-June. Primary language of instruction is English; secondary language of instruction is Turkish. Current enrollment is 911; 36 percent of faculty are U.S. nationals.
Opportunities: Four to 12 positions for teachers of mathematics, science, English, and physical education on the secondary level.
Requirements: U.S. bachelor's degree in appropriate field is required; U.S. master's degree is preferred. Two years' teaching experience is preferred. Previous international experience is preferred. Current teaching certification is required.
For *TESL/TEFL:* U.S. bachelor's degree in English is required; U.S. master's degree in English is preferred. Two years' teaching experience is preferred. Previous international experience is preferred.
Duration: Two years; renewable.
Benefits: Salary is based upon experience; with bachelor's degree and no experience, net salary is $6,500. Two-week pre-assignment orientation. Transportation is included for appointee and dependents. Housing is included. Home leave is included every three years. Free tuition for dependent children, medical insurance, TIAA/CREF, and social security are provided.
Application: March 1.
Contact: Dr. A. Donn Kesselheim or Dr. Jayne Warner, Robert College of Istanbul, 380 Madison Ave., New York, NY 10017.

Tarsus American School,
P.K. 6, Tarsus, Turkey.
This private, coed secondary-level institution was founded in 1888. Academic calendar runs from September to June. Primary languages of instruction are English and Turkish. Current enrollment is 547; 60 percent of faculty are non-native; 30 percent of faculty are U.S. nationals.
Opportunities: About five positions annually for teachers of science, mathematics, and general subjects. About three teachers of English as a foreign language needed. All students are Turkish nationals.
Requirements: U.S. bachelor's degree in appropriate field is required. Previous teaching experience is preferred. U.S. or British teaching certification is required.
For *TESL/TEFL:* U.S. bachelor's degree in English is required. Previous teaching experience is preferred. Previous international experience is preferred.
Duration: Two years; renewable.
Benefits: Salary is 30,500 Turkish liras plus $308 per month. One-month pre-assignment orientation in Istanbul. Transportation is included for appointee only. Housing is included. Medical care and insurance are provided.
Application: No deadline.
Contact: Overseas Personnel Office, United Church Board World Ministries, 475 Riverside Dr., New York, NY 10115.

YEMEN

Sanaa International School,
Box 2002, Sanaa, Yemen Arab Republic.
This private, coed primary/secondary institution encompassing grades kindergarten through 10 was founded in 1971. Academic calendar runs from September to June. Primary language of instruction is English. Current enrollment is 225; 65 percent of faculty are U.S. nationals.

Opportunities: About four positions.

Requirements: U.S. bachelor's degree is required; U.S. master's degree is preferred. Two years' teaching experience is required; five years' is preferred. Previous international experience is preferred.

Duration: Two years; renewable annually.

Benefits: Salary is $13,200–$16,300 per year. Transportation is included for appointee and dependents. Housing is included. Tuition assistance for dependent children is available. Major medical plan is provided with $1,000 deductible. Annual $2,000 overseas allowance is available.

Contact: Mr. James E. Gilson, Director, Sanaa International School, Box 2002, Sanaa, Yemen Arab Republic.

EAST AND SOUTHEAST ASIA AND OCEANIA

MORE THAN ONE COUNTRY

Helen Keller International,
15 W. 16th St., New York, NY 10011.
This U.S.-based organization founded in 1915 serves teachers, administrators, curriculum developers, and researchers.
Opportunities: *Fiji, Indonesia, and Philippines Special Education Program.* One to five positions annually for education and rehabilitation of the blind, and blindness prevention education. Each assignment requires different skills. Recruitment is based on specific positions as available.
Requirements: U.S. master's degree is required. Foreign language proficiency is preferred. Previous teaching experience is required. Previous international experience is required.
Duration: Three years; renewable.
Benefits: Salary depends upon assignment. Pre-assignment orientation in New York. Transportation is included for appointee and dependents. Housing is included. Blue Cross and major medical is included. An automobile is generally provided.
Application: No set deadlines.
Contact: Judith Benjamin, Assistant to the Director, Helen Keller International, 15 W. 16th St., New York, NY 10011.

Yale-China Association,
905A Yale Station, New Haven, CT 06520.
This U.S.-based organization founded in 1901 serves U.S. adults interested in contemporary China, and Connecticut corporations engaged in U.S.-China trade. This organization also sponsors education-abroad programs for undergraduate and graduate students.
Opportunities: *Yale-China Bachelor Program.* Six positions annually in Hong Kong and People's Republic of China for teachers of English as a second/foreign language on the primary level.
Requirements: U.S. bachelor's degree from Yale University is required. Chinese language proficiency on the intermediate level is preferred. Previous teaching experience is preferred. Previous international experience is preferred. Experience equivalent to classroom teaching, such as informal tutorials, will be considered.
Duration: Two years; not renewable.
Benefits: Salary is $6,000–$12,000 per year. One-week pre-assignment orientation in New Haven, CT. Transportation is included for appointee only. Housing is included. Home leave is included. Stipend for language study or free instruction is provided. Basic medical care is provided by host institution; major medical is provided.
Application: January 18; notification by February 18.
Contact: John Bryan Starr, Executive Director, Yale-China Association, 905A Yale Station, New Haven, CT 06520.

YMCA of the U.S.A.,
Overseas Service Corps, International Division, 101 N. Wacker Dr., Chicago, IL 60606.
Opportunities: *Overseas Service Corps.* About 45 positions annually in Taiwan and Japan to teach conversational English to adults at YMCA English Language schools.
Requirements: U.S. bachelor's degree in liberal arts is required; U.S. master's or Ph.D. degree in applied linguistics is preferred. Chinese or Japanese language knowledge is helpful. Two years' teaching experience is preferred. Previous international experience is preferred. Demonstrated interest in Asian, Chinese, or Japanese studies and interest in working for service-oriented organization required.
Duration: Taiwan: one year; renewable. Japan: two years; renewable.
Benefits: Salary varies with qualifications. Five- to seven-day pre-assignment orientation in host country. Roundtrip transportation for Japan, one-way for Taiwan is included. Housing is included. Medical insurance and assistance with language study are provided.
Application: For Taiwan: March 15 for July placement; notification by May. For Japan: March 15 for August/September placement; notification by May, and November 15 for April placement; notification by January.

Contact: YMCA of the U.S.A., Overseas Service Corps, International Division, 101 N. Wacker Dr., Chicago, IL 60606.

AUSTRALIA

Department of Education and Youth Affairs,
P.O. Box 826, Woden, ACT, Australia, 2606.

Australian Consulate General,
636 Fifth Ave., New York, NY 10111.
   Academic calendar runs from February to December. Primary language of instruction is English. The Ministry and Permanent Mission to the U.N. report that there is no need for U.S. teachers, educational administrators, or teachers of English as a second/foreign language at the present time.

BANGLADESH

American International School/Dhaka,
c/o Dept. of State, Washington, DC 20520.
   This private, coed institution serving kindergarten through grade eight was founded in 1963. Academic calendar runs from September to June. Primary language of instruction is English; other languages of instruction are Bengal and French. Current enrollment is 304.
Opportunities: Three to four positions available. Faculty generally recruited from local, expatriate residents.
Requirements: U.S. bachelor's degree in education is required. Two years' teaching experience is required.
Duration: Two years; renewable for two years.
Benefits: Salary is based upon a scale. Transportation is included for appointee and dependents. Housing is included. Home leave is included. Free tuition at school is available; allowance for boarding school after grade eight is provided.
Application: Not given.
Contact: Dr. Stuart J. Young, Superintendent, American International School/Dhaka, Dept. of State, Washington, DC 20520.

CHINA, PEOPLE'S REPUBLIC OF

Embassy of the People's Republic of China,
2300 Connecticut Ave. NW, Washington, DC 20008.
   Primary language of instruction is Chinese.
   The Embassy reports that there is a definite need for teachers of English as a second/foreign language primarily on the university and professional education levels. Below is general information on faculty recruitment needs.
Opportunities: About 100 positions annually for teachers of English as a second/foreign language on university and professional levels.
Requirements: U.S. bachelor's degree is required; U.S. master's degree in literature is preferred; U.S. Ph.D. degree in literature, American studies is preferred. Three years' teaching experience is required. Previous international experience is preferred. Experience in teaching English as a second/foreign language or as a translator from English to Chinese is required.
Duration: Three months to one year; renewable.
Benefits: Salary is RMB 360–1,000 per month. Transportation is included for appointee and dependents under 12 years of age. Housing is included. Medical care is provided at no cost.
Application: July through November; notification in May.

Contact: Division of Education, Embassy of the People's Republic of China, 2300 Connecticut Ave. NW, Washington, DC 20008.

Consortium for International Cooperation in Higher Education (CICHE),

One Dupont Circle, Suite 616, Washington, DC 20036.

This U.S.-based organization founded in 1980 serves teachers, lecturers, TESL/TEFL, administrators, curriculum developers, and researchers.

Opportunities: *PRC English Language Professors Project.* Sixty to 80 positions annually for English language, literature, linguistics, rhetoric, writing, and American studies on the university, professional, and postsecondary vocational levels.

Requirements: U.S. master's degree in English or American studies is required; U.S. Ph.D. degree in linguistics is preferred. Five years' teaching experience is required. Previous international experience is preferred.

Duration: One year; renewable for one year.

Benefits: Salary is RMB 360–1,000 per month. Pre-assignment orientation. Transportation is included for appointee, spouse, and children under 12 years of age. Housing is included. Free medical care is provided. One-month vacation plus vacation allowance is included. Free transportation to and from work is provided. Excess baggage allowance is available. Thirty to 50 percent of salary must be converted to foreign currency.

Application: Open.

Contact: Frank Klassen, President, Consortium for International Cooperation in Higher Education (CICHE), One Dupont Circle, Suite 616, Washington, DC 20036.

Foundation for American-Chinese Cultural Exchanges,

Box 227, 525 W. 120th St., New York, NY 10027.

This U.S.-based organization founded in 1980 serves U.S. and Chinese teachers, lecturers, TESL/TEFL, students, and other professionals.

The Foundation does not actively recruit or act as a placement agency. It is, however, frequently asked by Chinese universities to suggest candidates for teaching—primarily English language positions. The Foundation does make arrangements for individual scholars to lecture, by invitation, in China.

The Foundation publishes *Horizons*, a quarterly newsletter on cultural and educational exchange between the United States and China. A conference, cosponsored by Chinese universities, on teaching English as a second language is planned for Summer 1984 in Shanghai.

Hamline University,

International Studies Center, St. Paul, MN 55104.

Hamline University and Peking University (Beijing) have enlarged their undergraduate student exchange to include a faculty exchange beginning with the 1983-84 academic year. During each term of the 1983-84 year, an economics faculty member from Hamline University will be teaching at Peking University, and a literature faculty member from Peking will be teaching at Hamline University.

International School of Beijing,

c/o American Embassy, 17 Guang Hua Lu, Beijing, People's Republic of China.

This private, coed primary-level institution was founded in 1980. Academic calendar runs from September to June. Primary language of instruction is English; other languages of instruction are Chinese and French. Current enrollment is 95; 35 percent of faculty are U.S. nationals. The school was founded by the Embassies of Australia, Canada, New Zealand, the United Kingdom, and the United States to provide education to foreign children aged five to 13. Faculty is recruited primarily from the United States and the United Kingdom. The curriculum is based on, but not limited to, the U.S. model. There are nine full-time and several part-time faculty members.

Opportunities: Four positions every two years for general primary education, and mathematics and science education for grades six through eight.

Requirements: U.S. bachelor's degree is required. Two years' teaching experience is required. Previous international experience is preferred. Only teaching couples without dependents are accepted due to accommodation limitations.

Duration: Two years; renewable.

Benefits: Salary is $11,445–$17,745. One-month pre-assignment orientation in Beijing. Transportation is included. Housing is included. Mid-tour leave to Kuala Lumpur, Malaysia is included. Major medical and medical repatriation insurance are provided.
Application: January; notification by March/April.
Contact: Mr. John Ritter, c/o American Embassy, 17 Guang Hua Lu, Beijing, People's Republic of China.

FIJI

Ministry of Education and Youth,
Selbourne St., Suva, Fiji.

Academic calendar runs from late January to early December. Primary language of instruction is English; secondary languages of instruction are Fijian and Hindi.

The Ministry reports a need for U.S. mathematics and physics teachers on the secondary level and engineering and business administration teachers on the vocational/technical (secondary) level.

Work permits are required and the Fijian Government is very strict in enforcing this requirement. These permits are issued by the Ministry of Home Affairs upon recommendation of the Ministry of Education and Youth. Dependents will not be permitted to work.
Requirements: U.S. bachelor's degree in appropriate discipline is required; U.S. master's degree is preferred. Previous international experience is preferred.
Duration: Three years; renewable annually.
Benefits: Salary is based upon qualifications and experience. Transportation is not included. Housing is not included; however, a housing allowance may be available in certain instances.
Application: July to November.
Contact: Dr. Ahmed Ali, Minister of Education and Youth, Selbourne St., Suva, Fiji.

U.S. Peace Corps in Fiji,
c/o American Embassy, Suva, Fiji.
Opportunities: *Education Program.* Two to seven positions annually for teachers of English as a second language on the university level. About 40 positions for teachers of various subjects on the secondary level (presently there are 20 Peace Corps volunteers at this level). There are also vocational/technical (postsecondary) positions at the Fiji Institute of Technology.
Requirements: U.S. bachelor's degree in appropriate discipline is required; U.S. master's degree is preferred; U.S. Ph.D. degree for university positions is preferred. Foreign language proficiency is preferred. Two to three years' teaching experience is preferred. For teaching of accounting/bookkeeping, practical experience is preferred.

For *TESL/TEFL:* U.S. bachelor's degree in linguistics is required; U.S. master's or Ph.D. degree in linguistics is preferred. Two to three years' teaching experience is preferred.
Duration: Two years; renewable for one year.
Benefits: Salary is a monthly allowance. One-week pre-assignment orientation in the U.S., eight to ten weeks in Fiji. Transportation is included for appointee and dependents. Housing is included. Medical insurance, education for dependent children are provided.
Application: Not given.
Contact: Recruitment Office, U.S. Peace Corps, 806 Connecticut Ave. NW, Washington, DC 20525.

INDONESIA

Embassy of the Republic of Indonesia,
2020 Massachusetts Ave. NW, Washington, DC 20036.

Academic calendar runs from July to May. Primary language of instruction is Bahasa Indonesia.

The Embassy reports a general need for U.S. teachers, lecturers, guidance counselors, and teachers of English as a second/foreign language on the university, professional, vocational/technical (postsecondary), and special education levels.

Requirements: U.S. master's degree is required; U.S. Ph.D. degree is preferred. Four years' teaching experience is required.

For *TESL/TEFL:* U.S. master's degree in English as a second language is required; U.S. Ph.D. degree in English as a second language is preferred. Previous international experience is preferred.

Duration: Undetermined.

Benefits: Salary is based upon experience, paid in Indonesian standard currency. Transportation is not included.

Contact: Direktorat Jenderal Perguruan Tinggi, Jln Jenderal Sudirman Pintu I Senayan, Jakarta, Indonesia, or Direktorat Jenderal P.D.M. Jln RS Fatmawati, Cipete, Jakarta, Indonesia.

Bandung International School,

Jl. Tersuan Pasteur, P.O. Box 132, Bandung, Indonesia.

This private, coed institution serving preschool through grade eight was founded in 1972. Academic calendar runs from September to June. Primary language of instruction is English; other languages of instruction are French and Indonesian. Current enrollment is 139; 95 percent of faculty are non-native; 15 percent of faculty are U.S. nationals. Faculty is primarily British and American.

The institution publishes several booklets useful to potential U.S. faculty, such as *Living and Teaching in Bandung* and *Expatriate Telephone Book.*

Opportunities: About two positions annually for general education and one position for a teacher of English as a second language.

Requirements: U.S. bachelor's degree in English is required. Indonesian language proficiency on the beginning or intermediate level is preferred. Two years' teaching experience is required. Previous international experience is preferred.

For *TESL/TEFL:* U.S. bachelor's degree in linguistics, applied linguistics, or English is preferred. Indonesian language proficiency on the beginning or intermediate level is required. Two years' teaching experience is required. Previous international experience is preferred.

Duration: Two years; renewable.

Benefits: Salary is $13,000–$18,000 per year. One-month pre-assignment orientation in Bandung. Transportation is included for appointee and dependents. Housing is included. Free tuition for dependent children. Medical allowance is provided. $1,500 settlement allowance and loan to purchase an automobile are available.

Application: April 30 for September; notification by June 16.

Contact: Principal, Bandung International School, Jl. Terusan Pasteur, P.O. Box 132, Bandung, Indonesia.

Experiment in International Living,

Kipling Rd., Brattleboro, VT 05301.

Opportunities: About 50 positions for teachers of English as a second language for Indochinese refugees being resettled in English-speaking countries. Other opportunities include prevocational skill training and providing cultural orientation to the United States. A similar operation in Thailand will cease operation in 1984.

Requirements: U.S. bachelor's degree in social sciences is required; U.S. master's degree in international studies is preferred. Indonesian language proficiency on any level is preferred. Previous teaching exerience is required. Previous international experience is required. For cultural orientation, experience with Southeast Asian refugees is preferred; for prevocational training, Peace Corps experience in math or science is preferred. Teacher-training experience is preferred to supervise Thai and Indonesian teachers hired locally. In Indonesia, no dependents or nonworking spouses are allowed.

For *TESL/TEFL:* U.S. master's degree in teaching English as a second language is required. Indonesian language proficiency on any level is preferred. One year's teaching experience is required. Previous international experience is required.

Duration: One year; renewable for six months or longer.

Benefits: Salary is $13,500 for teacher/supervisors. One- to two-day pre-assignment orientation in Brattleboro, VT. Transportation is included for appointee. Housing is included; everyone lives in the refugee camp. Major medical, group life insurance, short- and long-term disability, and physicals are provided. Housing and living allowance is provided.
Application: No deadline.
Contact: Mrs. Helju Batchelder, Experiment in International Living, Kipling Rd., Brattleboro, VT 05301.

International School of Lhokseumawe,
Tromol Pos 627, Medar, Sumatra, Indonesia.
This is a private, coed primary-level institution. Academic calendar runs from early September to early June. Primary language of instruction is English. Current enrollment is 53; 87 percent of faculty are U.S. nationals.
Opportunities: Recruitment generally done at annual employment conferences sponsored by International Schools Service (ISS).
Requirements: U.S. bachelor's degree and teacher's certification are required. Foreign language proficiency is preferred. Five years' teaching experience is preferred. Previous international experience is preferred.
Duration: One year; renewable.
Benefits: Salary is $15,000 per year and up. Transportation is not included. Housing is included. Home leave and free tuition for dependent children are included. Blue Cross is provided through ISS.
Application: Deadline and application fees set by ISS.
Contact: Mary Rabbitt, International Schools Services, P.O. Box 5910, Princeton, NJ 08540.

Porhimpunan Persahabatan Indonesia-Amerika,
Jl. Diponegoro 23, Kotak Pos 148, Medan, Indonesia.
This public, coed, binational center school was founded in 1972. Academic calendar runs continuously. Primary language of instruction is English. Current enrollment is 2,000; five percent of faculty are U.S. nationals.
Opportunities: Positions annually for teachers of English as a second/foreign language.
Requirements: U.S. bachelor's degree in English as a second/foreign language is required; U.S. master's degree in English as a second/foreign language is preferred. Indonesian language proficiency on the intermediate level is preferred. Five years' teaching experience is required. Previous international experience is preferred.
Duration: Two to three years; renewable.
Benefits: Salary is $15,000 per year. Transportation is included for appointee only. Housing is included. Health insurance is provided.
Application: Open.
Contact: USIS BPAO Medan, American Embassy (Box 1), APO San Francisco 96356.

JAPAN

American Academy,
24-11, Nishi-Gotanda, 2-chome, Shinagawa-Ku, Tokyo 145, Japan.
This is a private, coed, secondary-level and vocational institution. Academic calendar runs from April to March. Primary language of instruction is Japanese; secondary language of instruction is English. Current enrollment is 300; 10 percent of faculty are U.S. nationals.
Opportunities: Two positions annually for general education and two to five positions for teachers of English and English conversation classes. Teachers are not hired directly from abroad; however, foreign teachers living in Tokyo are considered.
Requirements: U.S. bachelor's degree in any field is required. More than three years' teaching experience is preferred. Previous international experience is preferred.
For *TESL/TEFL:* U.S. bachelor's degree in linguistics or applied linguistics is preferred. More than three years' teaching experience is preferred.
Duration: Two years; renewable.

Benefits: Salary is $3,000 yen. Transportation is not included. Housing is included. Educational allowances for dependent children and health insurance are provided.
Contact: American Academy, 24-11, Nishi-Gotanda, 2-chome, Shinagawa-Ku, Tokyo 145, Japan.

Center for Asian Studies,
University of Illinois, 1208 W. California, Urbana, IL 61801.
   The Center for Asian Studies manages a Year-in-Japan Program at Konan University in Kobe, Japan, in cooperation with several U.S. universities.
Opportunities: *Year-in-Japan Program.* One opening annually for field director, who serves as part-time administrator and part-time instructor.
Requirements: Faculty status at one of sponsoring institutions is required. Japanese language proficiency and knowledge of culture is required. Previous administrative experience is preferred.
Duration: One year; renewable.
Contact: Director, Center for Asian Studies, University of Illinois, 1208 W. California, Urbana, IL 61801.

Christian Academy in Japan,
1-2-14 Shinkawa Cho, Higashi Kurume Shi, Tokyo 203 Japan.
   This private, coed primary/secondary institution was founded in 1950. Academic calendar runs from September to early June. Primary language of instruction is English. Current enrollment is 295; 92 percent of faculty are non-native; 86 percent of faculty are U.S. nationals.
Opportunities: About ten positions for general educators on the primary level; teachers of mathematics, science, computers, and media on the secondary level; and industrial arts instructors on the vocational/secondary level. One teacher of English as a foreign language needed.
Requirements: U.S. bachelor's degree in education or appropriate field is required; U.S. master's degree in same or education administration is preferred. Japanese language proficiency on the beginning level is preferred. Two years' teaching experience is required. Previous international experience is preferred.
   For *TESL/TEFL:* U.S. bachelor's degree in education is required; U.S. master's degree in linguistics is preferred. Japanese language proficiency on the intermediate level is preferred. Two years' teaching experience is required. Previous international experience is preferred.
Duration: One year; renewable. Average tenure is ten years.
Benefits: Salary is $5,200–$11,700 for ten months. One-week pre-assignment orientation at school. Transportation may be included for appointee and dependents. Housing is not included; approximate cost of housing is $300–$500 per month. Financial assistance for in-service and authorized graduate programs is available.
Application: December.
Contact: Headmaster, Christian Academy in Japan, 1-2-14 Shinkawa Cho, Higashi Kurume Shi, Tokyo 203 Japan.

Council on International Educational Exchange (CIEE),
Sanno Grand Building 205, 2-14-2 Nagata-cho, Chiyoda-Ku, Tokyo 100, Japan.
Opportunities: *Mombusho English Fellows Program.* About 100 to 150 positions annually for teachers of English as a second language on the secondary and vocational (secondary) levels. Fellows are not officially employed as teachers, although teaching responsibilities are on par with regular teachers.
Requirements: U.S. bachelor's degree is required. Japanese language proficiency on the beginning level is preferred. Six months' teaching experience is preferred. Previous international experience is preferred.
Duration: One year; renewable annually.
Benefits: Salary is 3,600,000 yen (U.S. $15,000). Three and one-half-day pre-assignment orientation in Tokyo. Transportation is included for Fellow only. Housing is not included.
Application: January 15 for 1983–84; September for subsequent years; notification by April.

Contact: Lin Honor, Asia and Professional Programs, Council on International Educational Exchange (CIEE), 205 E. 42nd St., New York, NY 10017.

Fukuoka International School,
4-1-28 Maidashi, Higashi-Ku, Fukuoka shi, Japan 812.

This private, coed primary-level institution was founded in 1971. Academic calendar runs from September to June. Primary language of instruction is English. Current enrollment is 22; 66 percent of faculty are U.S. nationals.

There is no formal employment program for hiring U.S. educators. Listed is general information on faculty recruitment.

Opportunities: One position every other year. Total faculty consists of three full-time members. Faculty recruited mainly from those individuals presently residing in Japan.

Requirements: U.S. bachelor's degree in elementary education is required.

Duration: One year; renewable annually.

Benefits: Salary is based upon education and experience. Transportation is not included. Housing is not included; approximate cost of housing is $200 per month. Medical insurance is provided. After two years' teaching, one month's salary is put aside annually for severance/retirement fund.

Application: Not given.

Contact: Administrator, Fukuoka International School, 4-1-28 Maidashi, Higashi-Ku, Fukuoka shi, Japan 812.

Hiroshima International School,
2-6, 2-chome, Ushita-naka, Higashi-ku, Hiroshima-shi, 730, Japan.

This private, coed institution, primarily for foreign children living in Hiroshima, serving kindergarten through grade eight, was founded in 1962. Academic calendar runs from August to June; English-as-a-second language programs run from April to March. Primary language of instruction is English; secondary language of instruction is Japanese. Current enrollment is 225; 60 percent of faculty are non-native; 23 percent of faculty are U.S. nationals.

The school runs a series of language programs, including English as a second language, for 110 Japanese children on all primary/secondary levels, language classes and counseling services for about 40 Japanese children who have lived overseas for one to four years and speak English, and Japanese language instruction for about 20 foreign adults.

The school serves as the foreign community's center by publishing a monthly magazine and initiating a community club and international library.

Opportunities: One to three positions annually for primary education and one to five positions for teachers of English as a second language on the secondary level.

Requirements: U.S. bachelor's degree in liberal arts is required; U.S. master's or Ph.D. degree in liberal arts is preferred. Japanese language proficiency on the beginning level is preferred. Three years' teaching experience is required. Related practical experience will be considered. Previous international experience is preferred.

For *TESL/TEFL:* U.S. bachelor's, master's, or Ph.D. degree in linguistics, applied linguistics, or English is preferred. Japanese language proficiency on the beginning level is preferred. Three years' teaching experience is required. Previous international experience is preferred.

Duration: Two years; renewable for two years. For TESL/TEFL: one year; renewable for one year.

Benefits: Salary is $15,000–$35,000 per year. Two- to three-week pre-assignment orientation. Transportation is included for appointee and dependents. Housing is not included; approximate cost of housing is $330 per month. School pays deposit of four months' rent. Dependent children receive free tuition. Moving allowance of $1,350 and freight allowance of $1,500 is provided.

Application: January for elementary school; notification by March. November for TESL; notification by December 1.

Contact: Principal, Hiroshima International School, 2-6, 2-Chome, Ushita-naka, Higashi-ku, Hiroshima-shi, 730, Japan.

Interface,
Fortress Yotsuya 2F, 1-1 Yotsuya-Dori, Chikusa-Ku, Nagoya, 464, Japan.

This is a public school offering English as a second language instruction to children. Academic calendar runs from April to March. Primary language of instruction is English. Current enrollment is 500; 100 percent of faculty are U.S. nationals.

Opportunities: Four positions for teachers of English as a second language on the primary, secondary, and adult education levels.

Requirements: U.S. bachelor's degree in linguistics, applied linguistics, English, Japanese, or education is required. Japanese language proficiency on any level is preferred. Previous teaching experience is preferred. Previous international experience is preferred. Experience working with children is highly desirable.

Duration: One year; renewable.

Benefits: Salary is 180,000 yen per month plus 20,000 yen housing allowance per month. Two-day pre-assignment orientation in Nagoya. Transportation is not included. Housing is included. Full medical coverage is provided. Five weeks paid vacation is included annually.

Application: Open.

Contact: Ken Nakamura, Interface, Fortress Yotsuya 2F, 1-1 Yotsuya-Dori, Chikusa-ku, Nagoya 464, Japan.

International School of the Sacred Heart,

4-3-2, Hiroo, Shibuya-ku, Tokyo 150, Japan.

This private, female only primary/secondary institution was founded in 1908. Academic calendar runs from September to June. Primary language of instruction is English; other languages of instruction are French, Japanese, Spanish, and Latin. Current enrollment is 650.

There is no formal employment program for hiring U.S. educators. Listed is general information on faculty recruitment.

Opportunities: About 10 positions for general educators, including teachers of English as a second language on the primary/secondary level.

Requirements: U.S. bachelor's degree in appropriate field is required; U.S. master's degree is preferred. Two years' teaching experience is required. Previous international experience is preferred.

For *TESL/TEFL:* U.S. bachelor's or master's degree in applied linguistics is preferred. Previous international experience is preferred.

Duration: Varies; renewable for one year.

Benefits: Salary varies.

Contact: Sister Victoria Uy, Headmistress, International School of the Sacred Heart, 4-3-1, Hiroo, Shibuya-ku, Tokyo 150, Japan.

Kyoto International School,

11-1 Ushinomiya-cho, Yoshida, Sokyo-ku, Kyoto, Japan 606.

This is a private, coed primary-level school. Academic calendar runs from September to June. Primary language of instruction is English; Japanese taught as a second language. Current enrollment is 50; 75 percent of faculty are U.S. nationals.

There is no formal employment program for hiring U.S. educators. Listed is general information on faculty recruitment.

Opportunities: Maximum of four positions annually for teachers of kindergarten through grade eight. The school has total faculty of four teachers. Applicants must be able to teach two to three grade levels in one class.

Requirements: U.S. bachelor's degree in any field plus teaching certificate is required. Two years' teaching experience is required. Previous international experience is preferred.

Duration: Two years; renewable.

Benefits: Salary is 2,460,000–3,280,800 yen per year. Transportation is included. Housing is included. Medical insurance, which covers about 30 percent of costs, including dental, is provided. Utilities are paid at 11,000 yen. Transportation to and from school is provided.

Application: February; notification by April.

Contact: Ms. J. Stewart, Kyoto International School, 11-1 Ushinomiya-cho, Yoshida, Sakyo-ku, Kyoto, Japan 606.

Language Institute of Japan (LIOJ),
4-14-1 Shiroyama, Odawara T250 Japan.

This private, coed language institution was founded in 1967. Academic calendar runs from July to June. Primary language of instruction is English. Current enrollment is 600 per year; 90 percent of faculty are U.S. nationals. The school offers language courses on all levels, including total language immersion courses for professionals.

Opportunities: Four to five positions annually for English language instruction on all levels.

Requirements: U.S. bachelor's degree is required; U.S. master's degree is preferred. Any foreign language proficiency on the intermediate level is preferred. Two to three years' teaching experience is preferred. Previous international experience is preferred.

Duration: Two to three years; renewable for maximum three years.

Benefits: Salary is 300,000 yen per month (about $16,000–$18,000 per year). One and one-half-week pre-assignment orientation in Japan. Transportation is included. Housing is not included; approximate cost of housing is $250 per month. National health insurance is provided. Seven weeks annual vacation is included.

Application: January 10.

Contact: P. Lance Knowles, Director, Language Institute of Japan (LIOJ), 4-14-1 Shiroyama, Odawara T250, Japan.

Marist Brothers International School,
2-1 1-chome, Chimori-cho, Suma-ku, Kobe 654, Japan.

This private, coed primary/secondary institution was founded in 1951. Academic calendar runs from September to June. Primary language of instruction is English; secondary language of instruction is Japanese. Current enrollment is 325; 50 percent of faculty are non-native; 50 percent of faculty are U.S. nationals.

There is no formal employment program for hiring U.S. educators. Listed is general information on faculty recruitment.

Requirements: U.S. bachelor's degree in English or English as a second language is preferred. Two years' teaching experience is preferred. Previous international experience is preferred.

Duration: Two years; renewable.

Benefits: Salary is based upon teaching experience. Transportation is included for appointee only. Housing is not included; allowance is provided. Tuition reduction is available for dependent children. Home leave is provided every two years. Local transportation and medical insurance are provided.

Application: February; notification by March/April.

Contact: Principal, Marist Brothers International School, 2-1 1-chome, Chimori-cho, Suma-ku, Kobe 654, Japan.

Nagoya International School,
2686 Minamihara, Nakashidami, Moriyama-ku, Nagoya, Japan 463.

This private, coed primary/secondary institution was founded in 1964. Academic calendar runs from September to June. Primary language of instruction is English; instruction is in Japanese only in language classes. Current enrollment is 220; 23 percent of faculty are non-native; 77 percent of faculty are U.S. nationals.

Opportunities: Four to five positions annually for teachers of self-contained classroom grades kindergarten through six and general secondary education. One teacher of English as a second language needed annually for intensive English as a second language program and night school.

Requirements: U.S. bachelor's degree in education is required. Japanese language proficiency is preferred. Two years' teaching experience is required. Previous international experience is preferred.

For *TESL/TEFL:* U.S. bachelor's degree in linguistics is preferred. Japanese language proficiency is preferred. Previous teaching experience is required.

Duration: Two years; renewable annually.

Benefits: Salary is $12,348–$17,391 based upon degree. Two-day pre-assignment orientation at school. Transportation is included for appointee and dependents. Housing is included. Free tuition for dependent children is included. Medical insurance costs are shared by appointee and school.

Application: February.

Contact: Robert N. Whitaker, Headmaster, Nagoya International School, 2686 Minamihara, Nakashidami, Moriyama-ku, Nagoya, Japan 463.

Nichibei Kaiwa Gakuin/International Education Center,
21, Yotsuya 1-chome, Shinjuku-ku, Tokyo, Japan 160.

This private, coed vocational/technical (secondary) institution was founded in 1945. Academic calendar runs from April to March. Primary language of instruction is English; secondary language of instruction is Japanese. Current enrollment is 2,000; 80 percent of faculty are non-native; 75 percent of faculty are U.S. nationals.

Opportunities: Five to ten positions annually for teachers of English as a second/foreign language and business on the vocational/technical (secondary) level and teachers of English as a second/foreign language, business administration, business law, and international law on the extension/adult education level.

Requirements: U.S. master's degree in social sciences is required; U.S. master's degree in social sciences is preferred. Japanese language proficiency on the intermediate level is preferred. Two years' teaching experience is required.

For *TESL/TEFL:* U.S. master's degree in linguistics or applied linguistics is required; U.S. Ph.D. degree in same is preferred. Japanese language proficiency on the intermediate level is preferred. Two years' teaching experience is required. Previous international experience is required.

Duration: Two years; renewable.

Benefits: Salary is minimum 4,200,000 yen per year. Return transportation is included upon completion of initial contract. Housing is not included; school assists in locating housing. Approximate cost of housing is 60,000–80,000 yen per month. Health insurance and pension costs are shared by school and appointee.

Application: Open. Write for brochure entitled *International Education Center* for details on programs and courses.

Contact: Takashi Suzuki, Director, Personnel Affairs, Nichibei, Kaiwa Gakuin/International Education Center, 21, Yotsuya 1-chome, Shinjuku-ku, Tokyo, Japan 160.

St. Mary's International School,
6-19, Seta 1-chome, Setagaya-ku, Tokyo 158, Japan.

This private, male only primary/secondary institution, offering the international baccalaureate, was founded in 1952. Academic calendar runs from September to June. Primary language of instruction is English. Current enrollment is 830; 90 percent of faculty are non-native; 60 percent of faculty are U.S. nationals.

Opportunities: Four to five positions for teachers of mathematics, science, and computers on the secondary level.

Requirements: U.S. bachelor's degree for elementary-level teaching is required; U.S. master's degree for secondary-level teaching is required. Any foreign language proficiency is preferred. Three years' teaching experience is required. Previous international experience is preferred.

Duration: Indefinite.

Benefits: Salary is $20,000–$25,000 (payable in yen). Transportation is included for appointee and dependents. Housing is not included; approximate cost of housing is $400–$600 per month. Tuition for dependent children is paid at 10 percent. School pays for half of medical insurance. Faculty members receive monthly activities/sports allowance.

Application: Late January/early February; notification by April.

Contact: The Headmaster, St. Mary's International School, 6-19, Seta 1-chome, Setagaya-ku, Tokyo 158, Japan.

Tokyo YMCA College of English,
7 Mitoshiro-cho, Kanda, Chiyoda-ku, Tokyo 101, Japan.

This private, coed vocational/technical (postsecondary) institution was founded in 1890. Academic calendar runs from April to March. Primary language of instruction is Japanese; secondary language of instruction is English. Current enrollment is 1,286; 30 percent of faculty are non-native; 20 percent of faculty are U.S. nationals.

There is no formal employment program for hiring U.S. educators. Listed is general information on faculty recruitment.

Opportunities: Positions for well-disciplined teachers of English as a second/foreign language.
Requirements: U.S. bachelor's degree in linguistics, applied linguistics, or English is required; U.S. master's degree in same is preferred. Two years' teaching experience is required. Previous international experience is preferred.
Duration: Two to three years; renewable.
Benefits: Salary is 240,000–300,000 yen per month. One-week pre-assignment orientation in Tokyo. Transportation is included for appointee only. Housing is not included; approximate cost of housing is 70,000–80,000 yen per month. School pays for half of medical insurance.
Application: January.
Contact: Vice-President, Tokyo YMCA College of English, 7 Mitoshiro-cho, Kanda, Chiyoda-ku, Tokyo 101, Japan.

KOREA

Seoul Foreign School,
55 Yonhi Dong, Seoul, Korea 120.
This private, coed primary/secondary institution was founded in 1912. Academic calendar runs from August to June. Primary language of instruction is English. Current enrollment is 720; 98 percent of faculty are non-native; 90 percent of faculty are U.S. nationals.
Opportunities: Five to 15 positions annually for self-contained primary-level teachers and specialists in reading, art, physical education, English as a second language, and library. Secondary-level teachers needed in French, Spanish, social studies, English, mathematics, art, home economics, music, and computer science.
Requirements: U.S. bachelor's degree in relevant field is required; U.S. master's degree in relevant field is preferred. One year's teaching experience is required; two years' is preferred. A personal Christian commitment is required.
For *TESL/TEFL:* U.S. bachelor's degree in English instruction is required; U.S. master's degree in teaching English as a second/foreign language is preferred. One year's teaching experience is required; two years' is preferred.
Duration: Two years; renewable.
Benefits: Salary is $15,000–$19,500. Ten-day pre-assignment orientation at the school. Transportation is included for appointee and dependents. Housing is included. Tuition is waived for dependent children. School pays 80 percent of medical insurance. Home leave is included after two years. School donates five percent of salary to retirement fund.
Application: December 31; notification by early March.
Contact: Headmaster, Seoul Foreign School, 55 Yonhi Dong, Seoul, Korea 120.

Seoul International School,
4-1 Hwa Yang Dong, Song Dong Ku, Seoul 133, Korea.
This private, coed primary/secondary institution, also offering adult education extension courses, was founded in 1973. Academic calendar runs from late August to mid-June. Primary language of instruction is English. Current enrollment is 470; 90 percent of faculty are U.S. nationals.
Opportunities: Six to ten positions including two to three English as a second language or LEA (language experience) positions annually for teachers of kindergarten through grade eight and English as a second language/reading coordinator on primary level. CRASH lab (comprehension, reading, self-help), English as a second language and general education on secondary level. Teaching couples are preferred.
Requirements: U.S. bachelor's degree in education is required. U.S. master's degree in education or related field is preferred. Two years' teaching experience is preferred. Previous international experience is preferred.
For *TESL/TEFL:* U.S. bachelor's degree in education or related field is required; U.S. master's degree in education, reading, or English as a second language is preferred. Previous teaching experience is preferred. Previous international experience is preferred.

Duration: Two years; renewable.
Benefits: Salary is based upon point system which considers experience and education. Pre-assignment orientation. Transportation is included for appointee only. Housing is not included. Partial medical insurance is provided. Free transportation to and from school is included.
Application: May; notification by following Spring.
Contact: Mr. Edward B. Adams, Headmaster, or Mr. Rucci, Principal, Seoul International School, 4-1 Hwa Yang Dong, Song Dong Ku, Seoul 133, Korea.

NEPAL

Ministry of Education and Culture,
Curriculum Textbook and Supervision Development Centre, Harihar Bhawan, Pulchowk, Lalitpur, Nepal.

Academic calendar runs from March to December. Primary language of instruction is Nepalese; secondary language of instruction is English.

The Ministry reports a need for mathematics teachers, guidance counselors, and curriculum developers for primary/secondary education. There is also a need for teachers of English as a foreign language.

There is no formal employment program for hiring U.S. educators. Listed is general information on faculty recruitment.
Requirements: U.S. bachelor's degree in education is required; U.S. master's or Ph.D. degree in education is preferred. Five years' teaching experience is preferred. Previous international experience is preferred.

For *TESL/TEFL:* U.S. bachelor's, master's or Ph.D. degree in applied linguistics is preferred. Five years' teaching experience is preferred. Previous international experience is preferred.
Duration: Three years; renewable for two years.
Benefits: Volunteers preferred. One-month pre-assignment orientation in Nepal. Housing is included.
Contact: Chief, Curriculum Textbook and Supervision Development Centre, Ministry of Education and Culture, Harihar Bhawan, Pulchowk, Lalitpur, Nepal.

St. Xavier's School, Jawalakhel,
G.P.O. Box 50, Kathmandu, Nepal.

This private, male only, primary/secondary institution was founded in 1951 by Jesuit missionaries. Academic calendar runs from February to December. Primary language of instruction is Nepalese; secondary language of instruction is English. Current enrollment is 620; 20 percent of faculty are non-native; 15 percent of faculty are U.S. nationals.
Opportunities: Three positions for teachers of English on the primary level and English and physics on the secondary level. U.S. citizens are not hired by school; however, there are four to five U.S. volunteers. Volunteers are expected to be part of missionary program.
Requirements: U.S. bachelor's degree is required. Previous teaching experience is preferred. Previous international experience is preferred.

For *TESL/TEFL:* U.S. bachelor's degree is required. Previous teaching experience is preferred. Previous international experience is preferred.
Duration: Two years; renewable.
Benefits: Salary is 1,000 Ners per month. Three-month pre-assignment orientation in Nepal. Transportation is included for appointee only. Housing is included.
Application: July for following February; notification in August.
Contact: Principal, St. Xavier's School, Jawalakhel, G.P.O. Box 50, Kathmandu, Nepal.

NEW ZEALAND

Department of Education,
Private Bag, Wellington, New Zealand.

Embassy of New Zealand,
37 Observatory Circle NW, Washington, DC 20008.
Academic calendar runs from February to December. Primary language of instruction is English.
The Ministry and Embassy report that there is no need for U.S. teachers, administrators, or teachers of English as a second/foreign language at this time.

PAKISTAN

Ministry of Education,
Islamabad, Pakistan.
Academic calendar runs from September to May. Primary languages of instruction are Urdu and regional languages; secondary language of instruction is English.
The Ministry reports a need for U.S. teachers of English as a second/foreign language and curriculum developers on the university and professional education levels.
There is no formal employment program for hiring U.S. educators. Listed is general information on faculty recruitment.
Requirements: U.S. master's degree is required; U.S. Ph.D. degree is preferred. Urdu language proficiency on the intermediate level is preferred. Ten years' teaching experience is required. Previous international experience is preferred.
For *TESL/TEFL:* U.S. master's degree in linguistics or applied linguistics is required; U.S. master's degree is preferred. Urdu language proficiency on the intermediate level is preferred. Ten years' teaching experience is required. Previous international experience is preferred.
Duration: One to three years; renewable up to five years.
Benefits: Salary is fixed under some technical aid programs. Three- to five-day preassignment orientation. Transportation is included for appointee and dependents. Housing is not included. Home leave is included.
Contact: U.S.A.I.D., Islamabad, Pakistan.

Lahore American Society School,
Lahore, Dept. of State, Washington, DC 20520.
This private, coed primary/secondary institution was founded in 1956. Academic calendar runs from June to August. Primary language of instruction is English; secondary language of instruction is Urdu. Current enrollment is 260; 50 percent of faculty are U.S. nationals.
Opportunities: Twelve positions annually for general educators and one position for a teacher of English as a second/foreign language.
Requirements: U.S. bachelor's degree is required; U.S. master's degree is preferred. Three years' teaching experience is required. Previous international experience is preferred in an Islamic culture.
For *TESL/TEFL:* U.S. bachelor's degree in linguistics, applied linguistics, or English is required; U.S. master's degree in English as a second language is preferred. Three years' teaching experience is required. Previous international experience is preferred in an Islamic culture.
Duration: Two to three years; renewable for one to two years.
Benefits: Salary is $9,955 with bachelor's degree; $12,529 with master's degree (tax free). Transportation is included for appointee and dependents. Housing is included. Home leave is included after two years. Transportation to and from school is provided.
Application: December.
Contact: Mrs. Theresa Akmal, Superintendent, Attn: Administrative Officer, Lahore American Society School, Lahore, Dept. of State, Washington, DC 20520.

PAPUA NEW GUINEA

University of Papua New Guinea,
Box 320, University Post Office, Papua New Guinea.

The university recruits overseas staff through international advertisement and competitive selection procedures. A substantial number of overseas academic staff is recruited for agriculture, arts, education, law, medicine, and science. Administrative positions are recruited less often.

PHILIPPINES

Ministry of Education, Culture, and Sports,
Arroceros St., Manila, Philippines.
Primary language of instruction is Pilipino; secondary language of instruction is English.
The Ministry reports that there is no need for U.S. teachers, administrators, or teachers of English as a second/foreign language at the present time.

Maryknoll College Foundation, Inc.,
Katipunan Rd., Loyola Heights, Quezon City, Philippines.
This private, coed (for tertiary level) and female only (for primary/secondary level) institution was founded in 1926. Academic calendar runs from June to March. Primary language of instruction is English; secondary language of instruction is Pilipino. Current enrollment is 6,369.
There is no formal employment program for hiring U.S. educators. Listed is general information on faculty recruitment.
Requirements: U.S. master's degree is required for tertiary-level instruction. Previous teaching experience is preferred.
Duration: Five months; renewable by five-month semester intervals.
Benefits: Salary is 1,300 Philippine pesos per month ($118). Transportation is not included. Housing is not included; approximate cost of room and board is ₱700 per month.
Application: January for June.
Contact: Academic Dean, Maryknoll College Foundation, Inc., Katipunan Rd., Loyola Heights, Quezon City, Philippines.

SINGAPORE

Singapore American School,
60 Kings Rd., Singapore 1026.
This private, coed primary/secondary institution was founded in 1956. Academic calendar runs from September to June. Primary language of instruction is English; other languages of instruction are French, Spanish, Mandarin, Mialay, German, and Swedish. Current enrollment is 1,831; 73 percent of faculty are U.S. nationals.
Opportunities: Positions for teachers of primary/secondary subjects including teachers of English as a second language. Usually not more than three married couples and three unmarried persons hired as instructors annually.
Requirements: U.S. bachelor's degree is required; U.S. master's or Ph.D. degree is preferred. Two years' teaching experience is required. Previous international experience is preferred.
For *TESL/TEFL:* U.S. bachelor's degree in linguistics is preferred. Previous teaching experience is required. Previous international experience is preferred.
Duration: Two years; renewable for two years.
Benefits: Salary is about Singapore $38,000 per year. Transportation is included for appointee and dependents. Housing is not included. Free tuition for dependent children is available. Medical and life insurance are provided. Overseas living and relation allowance is included.
Application: Early November; notification by January.
Contact: The Superintendent, Singapore American School, 60 Kings Rd., Singapore 1026.

SOLOMON ISLANDS

Ministry of Education, Training, and Cultural Affairs,
Box 854, Honiara, Soloman Islands.

Academic calendar runs from January to November. Primary language of instruction is English.

The Ministry reports that teaching opportunities are only available through the Peace Corps Volunteer Program (see page 6). Volunteers primarily needed for vocational education of metalwork, mechanics, small engine, simple plumbing, and electric work. About four positions available per year.

SRI LANKA

Embassy of the Democratic Socialist Republic of Sri Lanka,
2148 Wyoming Ave. NW, Washington, DC 20008.

The Embassy reports that English teachers are needed; however, all recruitment is done through the United Nations Development Program or by the AID agencies in various donor countries. U.S. nationals should direct all inquiries to the Sri Lanka Desk Officer, U.S. Department of State, Washington, DC 20520. Individuals requiring specific information relating to a specific, individual concern should contact the Secretary, Ministry of Higher Education, 17, Ward Place, Colombo 7, Sri Lanka, or the Secretary, Ministry of Education, Malay Street, Colombo 2, Sri Lanka.

Overseas Children's School,
47 & 51, Muttiah Rd., Colombo 2, Sri Lanka.

This private, coed primary/secondary institution was founded in 1958. Academic calendar runs from September to June. Primary language of instruction is English. Current enrollment is 540; 25 percent of faculty are non-native; 10 percent of faculty are U.S. nationals.

Opportunities: Two positions for general educators and one position for a teacher of English as a second language.

Requirements: U.S. bachelor's degree is required; U.S. master's degree is preferred. Five years' teaching experience is required. Previous international experience is preferred.

For *TESL/TEFL:* U.S. master's degree in applied linguistics is preferred. Five years' teaching experience is required. Previous international experience is preferred.

Duration: Two years; renewable for two years. For TESL: one year; renewable for one year.

Benefits: Salary is $14,000 per year. Transportation is included for appointee and dependents. Housing is included.

Application: January for September; notification in April.

Contact: Headmaster, Overseas Children's School, 47 & 51, Muttiah Rd., Colombo 2, Sri Lanka.

TAIWAN, REPUBLIC OF CHINA

Morrison Christian Academy,
P.O. Box 27-24, Taichung, Taiwan, Republic of China.

This is a private, coed primary/secondary institution. Academic calendar runs from August 15 to May 30. Primary language of instruction is English. Current enrollment is 480; 85 percent of faculty are U.S. nationals.

Opportunities: Ten to 18 positions annually for general educators. Most of the faculty comes from church-affiliated missions.

Requirements: U.S. bachelor's degree is required; U.S. master's degree is preferred. Three years' teaching experience is preferred. Previous international experience is preferred.

Duration: Three years; renewable.

Benefits: Salary varies. Pre-assignment orientation. Transportation is included for appointee and dependents on a fixed schedule. Housing is not included.
Application: Varies.
Contact: Arthur L. Westcott, Superintendent, Morrison Christian Academy, P.O. Box 27-24, Taichung, Taiwan ROC 400.

National Sun Yat-Sen University,
70 Lien-Hai Rd., Kaohsiung, Taiwan, Republic of China.
   This public, coed university was founded in 1924. Academic calendar runs from August to July. Primary language of instruction is Chinese (Mandarin); secondary language of instruction is English; other languages are French, Japanese, German, and Spanish. Current enrollment is 626; five percent of faculty are non-native; three percent of faculty are U.S. nationals.
Opportunities: Two positions for teachers of English literature, linguistics, English conversation and laboratory within the Department of Foreign Languages and Literature.
Requirements: U.S. master's degree in applied linguistics or English is required; U.S. Ph.D. degree in same, linguistics, or comparative literature is preferred. Mandarin Chinese language proficiency on the beginning or intermediate level is preferred. One year's teaching experience is required.
Duration: One year; renewable.
Benefits: Salary varies according to status. Transportation is not included for lecturers or junior assistant professors. Housing is included. Sixty-five percent of a comprehensive insurance packet is paid by the university.
Application: May 1; notification by mid-July.
Contact: Search Committee, Dept. of Foreign Languages and Literature, National Sun Yat-Sen University, 70 Lin-Hai Rd., Kaohsiung, Taiwan.

Taipei American School,
731, Wen Lin Rd., Sec. 1, Shih Lin, Taipei, Taiwan 111 Republic of China.
   This private, coed primary/secondary institution, also offering adult education, affiliated with Michigan State University, was founded in 1949. Academic calendar runs from late August to early June. Primary language of instruction is English; other languages of instruction are Chinese, French, German, and Spanish. Current enrollment is 1,086; 93 percent of faculty are U.S. nationals.
Opportunities: About 12 positions annually for teachers of grades kindergarten through 12. The school also employs one shop teacher, one business teacher, one computer instructor, and a part-time home economics teacher. There are five teachers of English as a second language on staff. In addition, there are two special education teachers. Michigan State University offers six courses annually.
Requirements: U.S. bachelor's degree is required; U.S. master's or Ph.D. degree is preferred. Foreign language proficiency on the advanced level is required for language teachers. Two years' teaching experience is required. Previous international experience is preferred. Teaching certification is required.
   For *TESL/TEFL:* U.S. bachelor's degree in linguistics or applied linguistics is required; U.S. master's or Ph.D. degree in same is preferred. Most teachers have advanced degrees. Two years' teaching experience is required. Previous international experience is preferred.
Duration: Two years; renewable annually.
Benefits: Salary schedule is based upon experience and education. One-week pre-assignment orientation at school. Transportation is included for appointee and dependents. Housing is not included; however, annual housing allowance is provided at $3,762 for single appointee, $4,158 for married appointee, and $4,554 for married appointee with children. Free tuition for dependent children is available. Home leave is provided after two years. Blue Cross/Blue Shield, life insurance and major medical plan are provided. Overseas allowance (seven percent of base salary) and relocation/settling-in allowance are included.
Application: December 1.
Contact: Ms. Vicky Shaw, Personnel Director, Taipei American School, 731, Wen Lin Rd., Sec. 1, Shih Lin, Taipei, Taiwan 111 Republic of China.

Tamkang University,
Institute of American Studies, Kinhua St., Taipei, Taiwan.

This private, coed university and teachers' college was founded in 1971. Academic calendar runs from September to August. Primary language of instruction is English. Current enrollment is 50; 50 percent of faculty are U.S. nationals.

There is no formal employment program for hiring U.S. educators. Listed is general information on faculty recruitment.

Requirements: U.S. Ph.D. degree is required. Foreign language proficiency is preferred.

Duration: One to two years; renewable.

Contact: Clement C. P. Chang, President, Tamkang University, Institute of American Studies, Kinhua St., Taipei, Taiwan.

WESTERN SAMOA

Department of Education,
P.O. Box 201, Apia, Western Samoa.

Academic calendar runs from January/February to mid-December. Primary language of instruction is Samoan; secondary language of instruction is English.

The Ministry reports a need for U.S. teachers, technical instructors, lecturers, teachers of English as a second/foreign language, researchers, and curriculum developers on all educational levels.

Listed is general information on faculty recruitment. Recruitment is also done through the Peace Corps Volunteer Program (see page 6).

Opportunities: Ten to 30 positions annually through the *Peace Corps Volunteer Program.*

Requirements: U.S. bachelor's degree is required; U.S. master's degree is preferred. Five years' teaching experience is required.

For *TESL/TEFL:* U.S. bachelor's or master's degree in English is required. Five years' teaching experience is preferred. In lieu of teaching experience, technical and vocational experience is accepted.

Duration: Two years; renewable.

Contact: Ministry of Foreign Affairs, Apia, Western Samoa, or the Secretary, Public Service Commission, Apia, Western Samoa.

EUROPE

MORE THAN ONE COUNTRY

Boston University,
Overseas Programs, 143 Bay State Rd., Boston, MA 00215.
Boston University's Overseas Program recruits, under contract with the U.S. Army and Air Force, U.S. teachers to provide graduate degree programs to military and civilian personnel at 49 locations in five countries: Belgium, England, Italy, the Netherlands, and West Germany.
Opportunities: *Overseas Programs.* Thirty-two positions annually for teachers of business administration, computer information systems, counseling, human services, international relations, and mechanical engineering on the graduate level. All courses are offered in the evenings and on weekends at military posts. Most assignments require two to three different course preparations during the year.
Requirements: U.S. Ph.D. degree in relevant discipline is required. Previous teaching experience on the graduate level is required. Previous international experience is preferred. All appointees are subject to a national agency check; a low-level security clearance is required.
Duration: One year; renewable for one year.
Benefits: Salary varies according to discipline, rank, and experience. Two-day pre-assignment orientation in Boston. Transportation is included for appointee, spouse, and two dependent children. Furnished housing is included. One-half tuition for two children at Department of Defense Dependent School is included. Medical and group life insurance and TIAA/CREF are provided. Military I.D. card provides privileges in PX, commissary, and recreational facilities.
Application: Open. Include application, resume, three letters of reference, and placement file (from college where last degree was completed).
Contact: Boston University, Overseas Programs, 143 Bay State Rd., Boston, MA 02215.

AUSTRIA

Austrian Embassy,
2343 Massachusetts Ave. NW, Washington, DC 20008.

Bundesministerium für Unterricht und Kunst (Ministry of Education and Arts),
Minoritenplatz 5, A-1014, Vienna, Austria.
Academic calendar runs from September to June. Primary language of instruction is German.
The Ministry and Embassy report that all programs for employing U.S. teachers are implemented through the Austrian-American Education Commission (see below) or through the *Fulbright-Hays Program* administered by the Council for International Exchange of Scholars (CIES) (see page 3).
Teaching positions at individual Austrian schools are offered through the state school authorities of the various states of Austria. Appointments are made throughout the school year based on demand. The salary is about 7.000 Austrian schillings per month. A small deduction is taken for health insurance. A list of the school boards is available from the Austrian Embassy.

Austrian-American Educational Commission (Fulbright Commission),
Schmidgasse 4, A-1082 Vienna, Austria.
The Fulbright Commission reports two programs for U.S. teachers of English as a foreign language.
Opportunities: *Teaching Positions.* Positions annually for teachers of English as a second/foreign language on the secondary level. Each teacher is responsible for 17 hours' instruction per week; schooldays are Monday to Saturday, classes are held mornings only. Teachers may be assigned to two schools in one city.
Requirements: U.S. bachelor's degree is required; teaching certification is required. German language proficiency is required. Previous teaching experience is required.
Duration: One year; renewable.

Benefits: Salary is 12.365 Austrian schillings per month less a small deduction for health insurance. Transportation is not included.

Application: March 1 for following year, notification by mid-May. Include application in German outlining career goals, two resumes in German, three letters of reference, academic transcripts, copy of teaching certification, proof of previous teaching experience, and certificate of German-language proficiency.

Contact: Anton Porhansl, Executive Secretary, Austrian-American Educational Commission (Fulbright Commission), Schmidgasse 4, A-1082 Vienna, Austria. Final selection of candidates and teaching assignments are made by the Austrian Ministry of Education and Arts.

Opportunities: *Teaching Assistantships.* Fifty positions annually for teachers of English as a second/foreign language on the secondary level. Each teacher is responsible for 12 hours' instruction per week. Morning classes only. Limited positions only are available in Vienna, Salzburg or Graz; applicants should be willing to accept positions in smaller communities.

Requirements: U.S. bachelor's degree in English or languages is required. German language proficiency is required.

Duration: One year; renewable for one year.

Benefits: Salary is 11.157 Austrian schillings (US $656) per month, minus a small deduction for health insurance. Transportation is not included. Position allows candidates to continue studies while they teach.

Application: March 1 for following year. Notification by May 1. Include application in German outlining study plans in Austria and career goals, two resumes, three letters of reference, academic transcripts, and certificate of German-language proficiency.

Contact: Anton Porhansl, Executive Secretary, Austrian-American Educational Commission (Fulbright Commission), Schmidgasse 14, A-1082 Vienna, Austria. Final selection of candidates is made by Austrian Ministry of Education and Arts.

BELGIUM

Commission for Educational Exchange between the U.S.A., Belgium, and Luxembourg,
Rue de Marteau, 21-1040, Brussels, Belgium.

The Fulbright Commission reports that opportunities for U.S. teachers are limited; the commission does finance a few positions through the *Fulbright-Hays Program.* Instruction is generally in English; however, beginning French or Dutch is required. For information, contact Council for International Exchange of Scholars (see page 3).

There are some private English-language schools in Belgium that regularly employ U.S. teachers (see *Schools Abroad of Interest to Americans* in Bibliography).

The U.S. Government does operate schools in Brussels for children of U.S. government and NATO employees. For information, contact Office of Educational Administration and Recruitment, U.S. Dept. of Defense, Washington, DC 20301 (see page 3).

Teaching positions in Belgium are sometimes available through International Schools Services (see page 4).

Any foreigner going to Belgium for more than three months must have a Belgian visa. Foreign teachers need work permits obtained for them by the employer, a process which takes a minimum of two months.

International School of Brussels,
19 Kattenberg, Brussels 1170, Belgium.

This private, coed primary/secondary institution was founded in 1951. Academic calendar runs from September to June. Primary language of instruction is English; secondary language of instruction is French. Current enrollment is 950; 88 percent of faculty are non-native; 60 percent of faculty are U.S. nationals.

Opportunities: Five to ten positions for teachers annually, including positions for teachers of English as a second/foreign language.

Requirements: U.S. bachelor's degree is required. U.S. master's degree is preferred. French language proficiency on the intermediate level is preferred. Previous teaching experience is preferred.

For *TESL/TEFL:* U.S. bachelor's or master's degree in linguistics is preferred. French language proficiency on the intermediate level is preferred. Previous teaching experience is preferred.

Duration: Two to three years; renewable. TESL/TEFL: one year; renewable.

Benefits: Salary is 700,000–1,100,000 Belgian francs annually. Transportation is included for appointee and dependents. Housing is not included; approximate cost of housing is 10,000–20,000 BF per month. School assists in finding housing. Dependent children receive free school tuition. Medical insurance is provided.

Application: Open.

Contact: The Superintendent, International School of Brussels, 19 Kattenberg, Brussels 1170, Belgium.

BULGARIA

Anglo-American School, Sofia,
8 Studen Kladonez, Sofia, Bulgaria.

This private, coed institution serving kindergarten through grade eight was founded in 1967. Academic calendar runs from September to June. Primary language of instruction is English; secondary language of instruction is Bulgarian; other language of instruction is French. Current enrollment is 84; 33 percent of faculty are U.S. nationals.

There is no formal program for hiring U.S. educators. Listed is general information on faculty recruitment.

Opportunities: Positions for teachers, administrators and teachers of English as a foreign language on the elementary level.

Requirements: U.S. bachelor's degree is required for teachers; U.S. master's degree in education administration is required for director; U.S. Ph.D. degree in education administration is preferred. Two years' teaching experience is required. Previous international experience is preferred.

For *TESL/TEFL:* U.S. bachelor's degree in teaching English as a second/foreign language is required. Two years' teaching experience is required. Previous international experience is preferred.

Duration: Four years; renewable.

Benefits: Salary is $14,000–$16,000 for teachers and teachers of English as a second/foreign language; $28,000 for administrators. Transportation is included for appointee and dependents. Housing is included. Educational opportunities for staff are encouraged. Medical and life insurance is provided.

Application: March 1.

Contact: Director, Anglo-American School, Sofia, 8 Studen Kladonez, Sofia, Bulgaria.

CZECHOSLOVAKIA

U.S. Information Service,
American Embassy, Prague, Czechoslovakia.

The USIS Office reports that opportunities for teachers of English as a second language exist through two programs: the *Fulbright-Hays Program*, administered by the Council for the International Exchange of Scholars (see page 3), and *English Teaching Seminars.*

The latter is organized during the summer by the Press and Culture Section of the U.S. Embassy in cooperation with the British Council and the Czech and Slavic Ministries of Education. Each seminar lasts two weeks and is designed to teach English to Czechoslovakian teachers. For more information, contact Office of Education Programs, U.S. Information Agency, Washington, DC 20547.

Opportunities: *Fulbright-Hays Program.* Two positions for teachers of English as a second language on the university level.

Requirements: Czech or Slavic language proficiency is preferred. Previous teaching experience is required.
Duration: Ten months; not renewable.
Benefits: Salary is $20,080–$22,620. Housing is included.
Application: September 15.
Contact: Council for International Exchange of Scholars, 11 Dupont Circle, Washington, DC 20036.

International School of Prague,
c/o American Embassy, Trziste 15, 125 48 Prague 1, Czechoslovakia.

This private, coed primary-level institution was founded in 1948. Academic calendar runs from August to June. Primary language of instruction is English; other languages of instruction are German and French. Current enrollment is 100; 90 percent of faculty are U.S. nationals.
Opportunities: Ten positions annually for primary-level educators and one position available for a teacher of English as a second language for grades one through eight.
Requirements: U.S. bachelor's degree in elementary education is required. Two years' teaching experience is preferred. Previous international experience is preferred. Generally only teaching couples are hired, preferably without children.

For *TESL/TEFL:* U.S. bachelor's degree in linguistics is required. Two years' teaching experience is preferred. Previous international experience is preferred.
Duration: Two years; renewable annually.
Benefits: Salary is $9,940–$21,360. One-week pre-assignment orientation at school. Transportation is included for appointee and dependents. Housing is included. Home leave is included upon renewal of contract. Blue Cross/Blue Shield is provided. Baggage allowance of $800 is included at beginning and end of contract.
Application: February 1; notification by March.
Contact: Don O. Hill, Director, International School of Prague, Dept. of State, Washington, DC 20520.

FINLAND

Ministry of Education,
Rauhanilatu 4, 00170 Helsinki 17, Finland.

Academic calendar runs from September to May. Primary languages of instruction are Finnish and Swedish; other languages of instruction are English, German, French, and Russian.

The Ministry reports a need for U.S. teachers of English as a foreign language on the university level and for teachers of professional and adult/extension education.
Contact: U.S. Educational Foundation in Finland, Estela Esplanadi 22 A. 15, 00130 Helsinki 13, Finland; Finnish American Scholarship Committee, Mechelininkatu 10 A, 00100 Helsinki 10, Finland; or individual universities.

International School of Helsinki,
Hattulantie 2, SF-00550 Helsinki 55, Finland.

This private, coed primary-level institution was founded in 1963. Academic calendar runs from August to June. Primary language of instruction is English. Current enrollment is 60.
Opportunities: An average of two positions annually for teachers of mathematics, language arts, science, and music on the primary level. One position for a teacher of English as a second language available every other year. Faculty also recruited in Britain.
Requirements: U.S. bachelor's degree in education and teaching certification is required. Three years' teaching experience is required. Previous international experience is preferred.

For *TESL/TEFL:* TESL certification is required. Three years' teaching experience is required. Previous international experience is preferred.
Duration: Two years; renewable.

Benefits: Salary is $13,000–$17,400 per year. Transportation is included for appointee and dependents. Housing is included. Free tuition for dependent children is available. Medical care, retirement contributions, and disability insurance are provided.
Application: December 31; notification by April 1.
Contact: Headmaster, International School of Helsinki, Hattulantie 2, SF-00550 Helsinki 55, Finland.

Vittakivi International Center,
SF-14700 Hauho, Finland.
This private, coed adult-education institution was founded in 1951. Academic calendar runs from November to May. Primary language of instruction is Finnish; secondary language of instruction is English. Current enrollment is 42; 40 percent of faculty are non-native; 20 percent of faculty are U.S. nationals.
There is no formal employment program for hiring U.S. educators. Listed is general information on faculty recruitment.
Opportunities: Positions annually for teachers of adult and continuing education. Average course lasts two to three weeks.
Requirements: U.S. bachelor's degree is required. Finnish language proficiency on the intermediate level is preferred. Previous teaching experience is preferred. Previous international experience is preferred.
For *TESL/TEFL:* U.S. bachelor's degree is required. Finnish language proficiency on the intermediate level is preferred. Previous teaching experience is preferred. Previous international experience is preferred.
Benefits: Salary is about 60 Finnish markkas per hour. Transportation is not included. Housing is included. Doctor's visits are paid for; medicines and hospitalization are not.
Application: Open.
Contact: Albert Szabó, Viittakivi International Center, SF-14700 Hauho, Finland.

FRANCE

French Embassy, Cultural Service,
4400 Jenifer St. NW, Washington, DC 20015.

French Cultural Services,
972 Fifth Ave., New York, NY 10021.
Academic calendar runs from September to June. Primary language of instruction is French.
The Embassy and Permanent Mission to the U.N. report that primarily only French citizens may teach at French primary and secondary schools. There are opportunities for U.S. nationals to teach in France through the *Fulbright-Hays Program* and the IIE-administered *French Teaching Assistants Program* (see below and page 61).

Franco-American Commission for Educational Exchange,
9 Rue Chardin, 75016 Paris, France.
Opportunities: *Fulbright Teacher Exchange Program.* Fifteen positions annually for teachers of English as a foreign language, literature and civilization, and American literature at the junior and senior high school level in France. This is a formal exchange between French secondary school teachers and U.S. secondary school teachers, junior college instructors, and assistant professors of French, all of whom have experience teaching English as a second language.
Requirements: U.S. bachelor's degree in French or English is required. French language proficiency on the advanced level is required. Three years' teaching experience is required. Candidates should have the ability to adapt to a different culture and educational system.
Duration: One academic year; not renewable.
Benefits: Participating U.S. and French teachers retain own salaries. Three-day pre-assignment orientation in Washington, DC and San Francisco. Transportation is included; it is paid in francs after arrival in France. Participants may exchange housing; approximate cost of housing is 3,000–4,000 French francs per month. Medical insurance up to $2,000 is provided for grantee only.

Application: November 1; notification by March/April.
Contact: Teacher Exchange Program, Office of International Education, U.S. Dept. of Education, Washington, DC 20202.

Opportunities: *Fulbright Senior Scholar Program.* Eight positions annually for junior lectureships in French universities. Fields include American literature/studies, political science, U.S. law, economics, business administration, and urban planning. FACEE makes final candidate decisions.
Requirements: U.S. master's degree in appropriate field is required; U.S. Ph.D. degree is preferred. French language proficiency on the intermediate level is required. Two years' teaching experience is required. Candidates should have ability to adapt to a different culture and university system.
Duration: October to June; renewable.
Benefits: Salary is 68,250 French francs for nine months. One-day pre-assignment orientation in Paris. Transportation is included; it is paid in francs upon arrival in France. Housing is included in Paris only; approximate cost of housing is FF 3,000–4,000 per month. Allowance of FF 4,550 per dependent (maximum two dependents) is granted. Medical insurance up to $2,000 is provided for grantee only.
Application: December 1; notification by April.
Contact: Council for International Exchange of Scholars, 11 Dupont Circle, Washington, DC 20036.

American Association of Teachers of French (AATF),
57 E. Armory Ave., Champaign, IL 61820.
   This U.S.-based organization founded in 1927 serves an individual membership of teachers. In addition to the exchange program described below, AATF maintains a monthly Placement Bureau Vacancy List for members. This list primarily describes U.S. vacancies but occasionally lists Canadian or foreign positions. AATF publishes the *French Review* and the *AATF National Bulletin.*
Opportunities: *Teacher-Exchange Program.* Three to six positions annually on an exchange basis with French lycée teachers (grades 10 to 12) of English. Program is sponsored jointly by AATF, French Ministry of Education, and the Foundation Franco-Américaine.
Requirements: Must be an AATF member. French language proficiency is required. Three years' teaching experience is required. Must have a full-time position at a public or nondenominational private secondary school or college.
Duration: One academic year; not renewable.
Benefits: Participants receive their regular salary from home school. Transportation allowance of 3,000 French francs is included by the Foundation Franco-Américaine. Housing, as well as automobiles, is usually offered as part of the exchange.
Application: February 1.
Contact: Philip Lee, American Association of Teachers of French (AATF), French Dept., Macalester College, St. Paul, MN 55105.

American International School on the Cote d'Azur,
Quartier de la Tour, La Baronne St. Laurent du Var, France.
   This is a private, coed primary/secondary institution. Academic calendar runs from September to June. Primary language of instruction is English; secondary language of instruction is French. Current enrollment is 96; 80 percent of faculty are non-native; 40 percent of faculty are U.S. nationals.
   There is no formal employment program for hiring U.S. educators. Listed is general information on faculty recruitment.
Opportunities: One position possible for teacher of mathematics, science, or English as a second language.
Requirements: U.S. bachelor's degree is required; U.S. master's or Ph.D. degree is preferred. French language proficiency on the intermediate level is preferred. Two years' teaching experience is required. Previous international experience is preferred.
   For *TESL/TEFL:* U.S. bachelor's, master's or Ph.D. degree in linguistics, applied linguistics or English literature is preferred. French language proficiency on the intermediate level is preferred. Two years' teaching experience is preferred.
Duration: One year; renewable annually.

Benefits: Salary is 4,800 French francs per month with increases based upon experience. Roundtrip transportation is included for appointee only. Housing is not included; approximate cost of apartments is 2,000 FF per month. Dependent children receive free tuition. Appointee receives French Social Security and medical insurance.
Application: March for following year.
Contact: Mr. Richard Graham, Headmaster, American International School on the Cote d'Azur, Quartier de la Tour, La Baronne St. Laurent du Var, France.

American School of Paris,
41 rue Pasteur, 92210 St. Cloud, France.

This private, coed primary/secondary institution granting an international baccalaureate was founded in 1946. Academic calendar runs from September to mid-June. Primary language of instruction is English; secondary language of instruction is French; other languages of instruction are German and Spanish. Current enrollment is 840; 86 percent of faculty is non-native; 70 percent of faculty are U.S. nationals.

There is no formal employment program for hiring U.S. educators. Listed is general information on faculty recruitment.
Requirements: U.S. bachelor's degree is required; U.S. master's degree is preferred. French language proficiency on the intermediate level is preferred. Two years' teaching experience is required. Previous international experience is preferred.

For *TESL/TEFL:* U.S. bachelor's degree in linguistics is preferred. French language proficiency on the intermediate level is preferred. Two years' teaching experience is required.
Duration: Two years; renewable. Tenure contract in third year.
Benefits: Salary is 110,000–185,000 French francs per year. Two-day pre-assignment orientation in Paris. Transportation is included for appointee only. Housing is not included; approximate cost of apartments is 3,500 FF per month. Free tuition for dependent children is available. Appointee receives French Social Security and medical insurance.
Application: Open; prefer March/April. Notification by late May.
Contact: Headmaster's Secretary, American School of Paris, 41 rue Pasteur, 92210 St. Cloud, France.

French and American Study Center,
10-14 boulevard Carnot, Lisieux 14104, France.

This institution offering intensive English and French language classes was founded in 1974. Academic calendar runs from late March to mid-November. Primary languages of instruction are French and English. Current enrollment is 150–200; 50 percent of faculty are U.S. nationals.
Opportunities: One or two positions available for teachers of French and for teachers of English.
Requirements: U.S. bachelor's degree is required; U.S. master's degree is preferred. Two years' teaching experience is preferred. Previous international experience is preferred.

For *TESL/TEFL:* U.S. master's or Ph.D. degree in applied linguistics is preferred. Two years' teaching experience is preferred.
Duration: One month; renewable.
Benefits: Salary is $1,000 plus room and board. One-week pre-assignment orientation. Transportation is included if appointee is coming with a group. Housing is included.
Application: Four months prior.
Contact: Dr. Ph. Almeras, Director, French and American Study Center, 10-14 boulevard Carnot, Lisieux 14104, France.

Institute of International Education (IIE),
809 United Nations Plaza, New York, NY 10017.

This U.S.-based organization founded in 1919 serves primarily as an administrative agency of exchange programs.
Opportunities: *French Government Teaching Assistantships.* Forty positions annually.
Requirements: U.S. bachelor's degree in French/English is preferred. French language proficiency on the advanced level is required. Previous teaching experience is not required.

Duration: Eight months; may be renewable.
Benefits: Salary is 3,700 French francs per month. One-week pre-assignment orientation in France. Transportation is not included. Housing may be included. Medical insurance is provided. Assistants may attend courses at local university with free tuition.
Application: January.
Contact: Study Abroad Programs, Institute of International Education (IIE), 809 United Nations Plaza, New York, NY 10017.

International School of Paris,
96 bis, Rue du Ranelagh, 75016 Paris, France.
Opportunities: Positions annually for teachers of history, science, and mathematics on the primary level.
Requirements: U.S. bachelor's degree is required; U.S. master's degree is preferred. French language proficiency is preferred. Two years' teaching experience is required. Previous international experience is preferred.

For *TESL/TEFL:* U.S. bachelor's degree in linguistics or teaching English as a foreign language is required. Two years' teaching experience is required.
Duration: Average is three to four years; renewable indefinitely.
Benefits: Salary is $14,000. Transportation is not included. Housing is not included; approximate cost of housing is $300 per month for a single person. Free tuition for dependent children is available. Medical, dental, and disability insurance is provided.
Application: April/May.
Contact: Mrs. P. Hayot, Principal, International School of Paris, 96 bis, Rue du Ranelagh, 75016 Paris, France.

Lycée International,
B.P. 128, 78104, Saint Germain en Laye, France.
This is a public, coed primary/secondary institution also offering extension education and postsecondary preparation for French business school examination. Academic calendar runs from September to June. Primary language of instruction is French. Current enrollment is 2,000; 30 percent of faculty are non-native; 10 percent of faculty are U.S. nationals.

The American section is a private, nonprofit association governed by the students' parents. The school is accredited by the French Ministry of National Education and is a member of the European Council of International Schools.
Opportunities: Two to three positions annually for teachers and administrators for the American section.
Requirements: U.S. bachelor's degree is required; U.S. master's degree is preferred. French language proficiency on the intermediate level is preferred. Previous teaching experience is preferred. Previous international experience is preferred.
Duration: Average is three to seven years; renewable.
Benefits: Salary is 7,800–11,630 French francs per month. Several-day pre-assignment orientation on campus. Transportation is not included. Housing is not included; approximate cost of a one-bedroom apartment is 2,500 FF per month. Free tuition for dependent children is available. French Social Security is provided. Five percent of annual salary is given as deferred compensation.
Application: February; notification by June.
Contact: Headmaster, Attn. American Section, Lycée International B.P. 128, 78104 Saint Germain en Laye, France.

GERMANY, DEMOCRATIC REPUBLIC OF

Embassy of the German Democratic Republic,
1717 Massachusetts Ave. NW, Washington, DC 20036.
Academic calendar runs from September to July. Primary language of instruction is German; secondary language of instruction is Russian.

The Embassy reports that there is no need for U.S. teachers, educational administrators, or teachers of English as a second/foreign language at the present time.

GERMANY, FEDERAL REPUBLIC OF

Commission for Educational Exchange between the U.S.A. and the Federal Republic of Germany,
Theaterplatz 1a, Postfach 200208, 5300 Bonn-Bad Godesberg, Federal Republic of Germany.

Academic calendar runs from August to June. Primary language of instruction is German; other languages of instruction are English and French.

The Fulbright Commission reports opportunities, including ones for teachers of English as a second/foreign language, through various components of the *Fulbright-Hays Program.*

Opportunities: *Teaching Assistantship Program.* About 20 positions available annually for teachers of English as a second language, primarily on secondary level. Primarily for U.S. students of German. Students will be assigned to German schools to teach/assist in English.

Requirements: U.S. bachelor's degree in linguistics, applied linguistics, English, or German is required; U.S. master's degree in same is preferred. German language proficiency is required. Previous teaching experience is preferred.

Duration: One year; not renewable.

Benefits: Salary is about 900 German marks per month. Four-day pre-assignment orientation in Bonn. Transportation is included for appointee only. Housing is not included; approximate cost of housing is $100–$150 per month. USIA group health and emergency accident insurance are included.

Application: By October 31 for following year; notification by June.

Contact: Study Abroad Programs Division, Institute of International Education, 809 United Nations Plaza, New York, NY 10017.

Opportunities: *Fulbright Lecturing Awards.* About 20 positions annually including positions for teachers of English as a second/foreign language, on university, professional, and vocational levels. Applicants are encouraged to identify a host institution in Germany; otherwise the Fulbright Commission will assist in placement negotiation.

Requirements: U.S. Ph.D. degree in field of assignment is required. German language proficiency is preferred. Several years' university teaching experience is required. Previous international experience is preferred.

For *TESL/TEFL:* U.S. bachelor's degree in linguistics, applied linguistics, American studies, or German is required; U.S. master's and Ph.D. degree in same is required. German language proficiency is preferred. Several years' university teaching experience is required.

Duration: Four to ten months; not renewable.

Benefits: Salary is monthly stipends up to 4,300 German marks. Three-day pre-assignment orientation in Bonn. Transportation is included for appointee only. Housing is not included; approximate cost of housing is $200–$300 per month. USIA group health and emergency accident insurance are provided.

Application: September 30; notification in March/April.

Contact: Dr. H. Jochen Hoffman, Program Officer, Council for International Exchange of Scholars, 11 Dupont Circle, Washington, DC 20036.

Opportunities: *Fulbright Interchange Teacher Program.* About 25 positions annually, including positions for teachers of English as a second/foreign language, on primary, secondary, and vocational levels.

Requirements: U.S. bachelor's degree in field of assignment is required; U.S. master's or Ph.D. degree is preferred. German language proficiency on the advanced level is required. Three years' teaching experience is required. Previous international experience is preferred.

For *TESL/TEFL:* U.S. bachelor's, master's, or Ph.D. degree in linguistics, applied linguistics, or English is preferred. German language proficiency on the advanced level is required. Three years' teaching experience is required.

Duration: One year; not renewable.

Benefits: Exchange is considered leave with pay; small supplement is available. Four-day pre-assignment orientation in Bonn. Transportation is included for appointee only. Housing is included if exchange partners agree; approximate cost of housing is $200–$400 per month. USIA group health and accident insurance are provided.

Application: October 15; notification in April.

Contact: Teacher Exchange Branch, International Education Programs, U.S. Dept. of Education, Washington, DC 20202.

Institute of International Education (IIE),
809 United Nations Plaza, New York, NY 10017.

This U.S.-based organization founded in 1919 serves primarily as an administrative agency for exchange programs.

Opportunities: *Padagagischer Austauschdienst Teaching Assistantships.* Twenty positions annually for teachers of English/American studies on the secondary level.

Requirements: U.S. bachelor's degree is required. German language proficiency on the intermediate/advanced level is required. Previous teaching experience is not required.

Duration: One academic year; not renewable.

Benefits: Salary is 900 German marks per month. Transportation is included as a Fulbright travel grant. Housing is not included. Health and accident insurance ($2,000) are provided.

Application: October 31; notification by June.

Contact: Study Abroad Programs Division, Institute of International Education (IIE), 809 United Nations Plaza, New York, NY 10017.

International School—Hamburg,
2000 Hamburg 52, Holmbrook 20, Federal Republic of Germany.

This private, coed primary/secondary institution was founded in 1957. Academic calendar runs from September to June. Primary language of instruction is English. Current enrollment is 530; 90 percent of faculty are non-native; 30 percent of faculty are U.S. nationals.

There is no formal employment program for hiring U.S. educators. Listed is general information on faculty recruitment.

Opportunities: About five positions annually for teachers on the primary and secondary levels.

Requirements: U.S. bachelor's degree is required. U.S. master's degree is preferred. German language proficiency on the intermediate level is preferred. Previous teaching experience is required. Previous international experience is preferred.

For *TESL/TEFL:* U.S. bachelor's degree in linguistics is required. U.S. master's degree in linguistics is preferred. German language proficiency on the intermediate level is preferred. Two years' teaching experience is required. Previous international experience is required.

Duration: Two years; renewable.

Benefits: Salary is about 50.000 German marks. Transportation is included for appointee and dependents. Housing is not included; approximate cost of housing is DM 600–700 per month (single). Dependent children receive free tuition. Medical benefits are provided.

Application: April 15.

Contact: Headmaster, International School—Hamburg, 2000 Hamburg 52, Holmbrook 20, Federal Republic of Germany.

John F. Kennedy Schule,
Teltowerdamm 87, 1000 Berlin 37, Federal Republic of Germany.

This is a public, coed primary/secondary institution. Academic calendar runs from August to July. Primary languages of instruction are German and English. Fifty percent of faculty are non-native; 50 percent of faculty are U.S. nationals.

Opportunities: Ten to 15 positions annually for teachers of mathematics, science and English composition on the secondary level.

Requirements: U.S. bachelor's degree is required; U.S. master's degree is required for secondary-level teaching, preferred for elementary-level teaching. German language proficiency on the advanced level is preferred. Two years' teaching experience is required. Teaching certification is required.

Duration: Two years; renewable for three years.

Benefits: Salary is based upon degree and age. Three-week pre-assignment orientation in Berlin. Transportation is included for appointee and dependents. Housing is not included. Home leave is included on contract renewal. Health insurance is provided. Appointees receive U.S. military PX and recreational facility privileges.

Application: January 30 for August term.

Contact: Managing Principal, John F. Kennedy Schule, Teltowerdamm 87, 1000 Berlin 37, Federal Republic of Germany.

GREECE

Consulate General of Greece,
69 E. 79th St., New York, NY 10021.

Academic calendar runs from September to June. Primary language of instruction is Greek.

The Permanent Mission to the U.N. reports that there is no need for teachers, educational administrators, or teachers of English as a second/foreign language at the present time. For information on obtaining employment at individual institutions, write directly to the school. A list of names and addresses can be found in *Schools Abroad of Interest to Americans* (see Bibliography).

American Community Schools of Athens,
129 Aghias Paraskevis St., 152 34 Halandri, Athens, Greece.

This private, coed primary/secondary institution was founded in 1946. Academic calendar runs from September to mid-June. Primary language of instruction is English; other languages of instruction are Greek, French, German, Spanish and Arabic. Current enrollment is 1,660; 77 percent of faculty are U.S. nationals.

Opportunities: About 18 to 20 positions annually for teachers in the following fields: elementary education; English, social studies, mathematics, science, and physical education on the secondary level; mechanical drawing/industrial arts on the vocational/secondary level; and remedial reading and learning disability specialists.

Requirements: U.S. bachelor's degree in appropriate field is required. Two years' teaching experience is required.

Duration: Three years; renewable.

Benefits: Salary is 1,185,103–2,109,716 drachmas based upon experience and degree. Two-day pre-assignment orientation at school. Transportation is included for appointee and dependents. Housing is not included; approximate cost of housing is 12,000 drachmas for a one-bedroom apartment. Faculty may receive 50 percent of tuition for graduate courses. Home leave is provided after two years. Medical insurance and Greek social security are provided. TIAA/CREF participation is available after two years.

Application: March; notification by mid-May.

Contact: Superintendent of Schools, American Community Schools of Athens, 129 Aghias Paraskevis St., 152 34 Halandri, Athens, Greece.

Anatolia College,
Thessaloniki, Greece.

This private, coed institution was founded in 1886. Academic calendar runs from September to June. Primary language of instruction is Greek; secondary language of instruction is English. Current enrollment is 1,500; 18 percent of faculty are non-native; 17 percent of faculty are U.S. nationals.

Opportunities: Four to five positions for teachers of English language and literature on the secondary level.

Requirements: U.S. bachelor's degree is required; U.S. master's degree is preferred. Two years' teaching experience is required. Previous international experience is preferred.

For *TESL/TEFL:* U.S. bachelor's degree is required; U.S. master's degree is preferred. Two years' teaching experience is preferred.

Duration: Three years; renewable for three years.

Benefits: Salary is 700,000 drachmas. Pre-assignment orientation on campus. Transportation is included for appointee and dependents. Housing is included. Free tuition for dependent children is available at local school with U.S. curriculum. Blue Cross and TIAA pension plan are provided.

Application: January 1; notification by late spring.

Contact: William W. McGrew, President, Anatolia College, Thessaloniki, Greece.

Hellenic American Union,
22 Massalias St., Athens, Greece.

Opportunities: *English Studies Program.* The Hellenic American Union employs 10 teachers of English as a foreign language and one administrator of this program. There are generally two to three positions available annually for U.S. teachers.

Requirements: U.S. bachelor's or master's degree in teaching English as a foreign language is required. Two to three years' teaching experience is required.

Duration: One year; renewable.

Benefits: Salary is 400 drachmas per hour. Transportation is not included. Housing is not included; approximate cost of housing is 10,000 drachmas per month. Language training on all levels is provided. Medical insurance is provided.

Application: May 1 for October.

Contact: Executive Director, Hellenic American Union, 22 Massalias St., Athens, Greece.

Pinewood Schools of Thessaloniki, Greece,
P.O. Box 21001–55510 Pilea, Thessaloniki, Greece.

This primary/secondary institution was founded in 1950. Academic calendar runs from September to June. Primary language of instruction is English; other languages of instruction are modern Greek and French. Current enrollment is 120; 73 percent of faculty are non-native; 47 percent of faculty are U.S. nationals.

There is no formal employment program for hiring U.S. educators. Listed is general information on faculty recruitment.

Opportunities: Two to three positions for general education teachers (grades kindergarten through eight) and English, science, and social studies teachers on the secondary level.

Requirements: U.S. bachelor's degree is required; U.S. master's degree is preferred. Two years' teaching experience is required. Previous international experience is preferred.

Duration: Two years; renewable for two years.

Benefits: Salary is minimum $7,800 per year with bachelor's degree. Transportation is included for appointee and dependents. Housing is not included; approximate cost of housing is 20,000 drachmas per month. Free tuition for maximum two dependent children is available. Comprehensive medical care and life insurance coverage are provided. Supplementary salary for certain extracurricular activities is included.

Application: March.

Contact: Peter B. Baiter, Director, Pinewood Schools of Thessaloniki, Greece, P.O. Box 21001–55510 Pilea, Thessaloniki, Greece.

HUNGARY

Embassy of the Hungarian People's Republic,
3910 Shoemaker St. NW, Washington, DC 20008.

Primary language of instruction is Hungarian.

The Embassy reports that there is a need for U.S. teachers and lecturers on the university level. There is a special need for U.S. teachers of English as a foreign language.

For information contact the U.S. Information Agency, 400 C St. SW, Washington, DC 20547.

ICELAND

U.S. Educational Foundation in Iceland,
P.O. Box 7133, Neshagi 16, Reykjavik, Iceland.
    Academic calendar runs from September to June. Primary language of instruction is Icelandic; secondary language of instruction is Danish; other languages of instruction are English, French, and German.
Opportunities: *Fulbright-Hays Program.* Three to four positions annually for university-level lecturers and researchers in American literature, nursing, and social sciences.
Requirements: U.S. Ph.D. degree in relevant field is preferred. Previous teaching experience is preferred. Previous international experience is required for nursing.
Duration: Four to eight months; not renewable unless grantee makes own arrangements with department.
Benefits: Salary is about $1,000–$1,500 per month. Five-day pre-assignment orientation in Iceland. Transportation is included for appointee only. Housing is not included; approximate cost of housing is $250–$300 per month. Icelandic government health care is provided.
Application: July for academic year beginning 14 months later.
Contact: Council for International Exchange of Scholars, 11 Dupont Circle, Washington, DC 20036.

IRELAND

Department of Education,
Marlborough St., Dublin 1, Ireland.
    Academic calendar runs from September to July. Primary language of instruction is English; secondary language of instruction is Irish; other languages of instruction are French, German, Italian, and Spanish.
    The Ministry reports that there is no need for U.S. teachers or administrators at the present time.

ITALY

Ministry of Education,
General Directorate for Cultural Exchanges, Via Ippolito Nievo, 35, 00153 Rome, Italy.

Commission for Cultural Exchange between Italy and the United States,
Via Boncompagni, 16, 00187 Rome, Italy.
    Academic calendar runs from September to June. Primary language of instruction is Italian; secondary language of instruction is English.
    The Ministry and Fulbright Commission report that Italian law prohibits the hiring of foreign teachers in state schools.
    There are several U.S. military dependents' schools. Information concerning faculty positions should be obtained from either Overseas Dependents Schools, U.S. Dept. of Defense, Washington, DC, or Directorate, U.S. Dependents Schools, European Area, Kanalweg 20, 75, Karlsruhe, Postfach 6969, Federal Republic of Germany.
    The European Council of International Schools, which represents over 120 private schools in Europe, largely U.S.-sponsored, assists its members in faculty recruitment. Information is available from its U.S. affiliate, Robert M. Sandoe and Associates, 29 Newbury St., Boston, MA 02116.

American International School in Genoa,
Via Quarto 13/C, 16148 Genoa, Italy.
    This private, coed primary-level institution was founded in 1963. Academic calendar runs from September to June. Primary language of instruction is English; secondary

language of instruction is Italian. Current enrollment is 72; 92 percent of faculty are non-native; 83 percent of faculty are U.S. nationals.

There is no formal employment program for hiring U.S. educators. Listed is general information on faculty recruitment.

Opportunities: Two to four positions annually for general education teachers of pre-kindergarten through grade eight.

Requirements: U.S. bachelor's degree in education is required. Two years' teaching experience is required.

Duration: Two years; renewable.

Benefits: Salary is 10,000,000–14,000,000 lire per year. Transportation is included for appointee only. Housing allowance of 2,000,000 lire is included. Italian state medical insurance is provided.

Contact: Principal, American International School in Genoa, Via Quarto 13/C, 16148 Genoa, Italy.

American School of Milan,
Villaggio Mirasole, 20090 Noverasco di Opera, Casella Postale 55, Milano, Italy.

This private, coed primary/secondary institution was founded in 1962. Academic calendar runs from September to June. Primary language of instruction is English; secondary language of instruction is Italian. Current enrollment is 450; 90 percent of faculty are U.S. nationals.

Opportunities: About 12 positions annually for teachers of general education. There are four instructors of English as a second language on staff. Facilities to assist learning-disabled students (on the elementary-school level) are available.

Requirements: U.S. bachelor's degree is required; U.S. master's degree is preferred. Two years' teaching experience is required. Previous international experience is preferred.

For *TESL/TEFL:* U.S. bachelor's or master's degree in linguistics is preferred. Two years' teaching experience is required.

Duration: Three years; renewable.

Benefits: Salary is 16,500,000 lire per year. Four-day pre-assignment orientation. Transportation is not included. Housing is not included; approximate cost of housing is 450,000–600,000 lire per month. Home leave is included after three years. Medical insurance and pension plan are provided.

Application: February 1.

Contact: Albert Chudler, Director, American School of Milan, Villaggio Mirasole, 20090 Noverasco di Opera, Casella Postale 55, Milano, Italy.

International School of Trieste,
Via Conconello 16, Opicina, Trieste, Italy.

This private, coed primary-level institution was founded in 1964. Academic calendar runs from September to June. Primary language of instruction is English; secondary language of instruction is Italian. Current enrollment is 112; 69 percent of faculty are non-native; 37 percent of faculty are U.S. nationals.

Opportunities: Between two and four positions annually. The school is a member of the European Council of International Schools, which acts as a recruitment service.

Requirements: U.S. bachelor's degree in elementary education is required; U.S. master's degree in mathematical science is preferred. Italian language proficiency on the beginning level is preferred. Two years' teaching experience is preferred. Previous international experience is preferred.

Duration: One to three years; renewable.

Benefits: Salary is about $10,000 (net) per year. Transportation is included for appointee only. Housing is not included; approximate cost of housing is $350 per month. Free tuition for dependent children is available. Medical care and hospitalization are provided. Free school lunches and transportation is included.

Application: Open; notification by May/June.

Contact: Daniel W. Sheehan, Director, International School of Trieste, Via Conconello 16, Opicina, Trieste, Italy.

School of Advanced International Studies, Johns Hopkins University,
Via Belmeloro 11, 40126, Bologna, Italy.

This private, coed graduate-level institution, founded in 1955, is an overseas campus of this U.S.-based university. Academic calendar runs from August to June. Primary language of instruction is English; secondary languages of instruction are French and Italian. Current enrollment is 110; 93 percent of faculty are non-native; 7 percent of faculty are U.S. nationals.

Opportunities: Two to three positions for teachers of international relations, international economics, and European studies on the graduate level.

Requirements: U.S. Ph.D. degree in social sciences or history is required. Italian or French language proficiency on the advanced level is required. Previous teaching experience is preferred. Previous international experience is preferred.

Duration: Three years; renewable.

Benefits: Salary is commensurate with U.S. salaries at the same rank. Transportation may be included for appointee and dependents. Housing is included. Blue Cross/Blue Shield, life insurance, and TIAA are included.

Application: Open; notification by March/April preceding fall semester.

Contact: Dean Robert A. Lystad, School of Advanced International Studies, Johns Hopkins University, 1740 Massachusetts Ave. NW, Washington, DC 20036; Robert G. Gard, Jr., School of Advanced International Studies, Bologna Center, Via Belmeloro 11, 40126, Bologna, Italy.

LUXEMBOURG

Ministry of National Education,
6, boulevard Royal, L-2910 Luxembourg.

Permanent Mission of Luxembourg.
801 Second Ave., New York, NY 10017.

Academic calendar runs from September to July. Primary language of instruction is German; secondary language of instruction is French.

The Ministry and Permanent Mission to the U.N. report that there is no need for U.S. teachers, administrators, or teachers of English as a second/foreign language at the present time.

MALTA

U.S. Information Service,
American Embassy, Valetta, Malta.

Opportunities: *Fulbright-Hays Program.* One position annually for a teacher of international business management on the university level.

Requirements: U.S. Ph.D. degree in business is required. Italian language proficiency is preferred. Five to 10 years' teaching experience is required. Previous international experience is preferred.

Duration: Nine months; not renewable.

Benefits: Salary is a fixed stipend. One- to two-week pre-assignment orientation in Washington, DC. Transportation is included for appointee and dependents. Housing is included for appointee and dependents. Local medical care is available at practically no cost.

Contact: Council on International Exchange of Scholars, 11 Dupont Circle, Washington, DC 20036.

NETHERLANDS

Ministry of Education and Science,
P.O. Box 20551, 2500 EN's, The Hague, Netherlands.

Academic calendar runs from September to September. Primary language of instruction is Dutch.

The Ministry reports that there is no need for U.S. teachers, educational administrators, or teachers of English as a second/foreign language at the present time.

American School of the Hague,
Doornstraat 6, 2584 AM, The Hague, Netherlands.
This private, coed primary/secondary institution was founded in 1953. Academic calendar runs from August to June. Primary language of instruction is English; other languages of instruction are French, German, Spanish, and Dutch. Current enrollment is 850; 80 percent of faculty are non-native; 80 percent of faculty are U.S. nationals.
Opportunities: Two to six positions for teachers of various fields on primary and secondary level.
Requirements: U.S. bachelor's degree plus fifth year of training, defined as master's degree or 30 semester hours of graduate work, are required. Two years' teaching experience is required. Teaching certification is required.
Duration: One year; renewable.
Benefits: Salary is 41.160–85.300 guilders (includes eight percent vacation pay) per year. One-week pre-assignment orientation at school. Transportation is not included. Housing is not included; approximate cost of housing is 1.50 guilders per month. Medical insurance is provided.
Application: January 15; notification by April.
Contact: Dr. Gail D. Schoppert, Superintendent, American School of the Hague, Doornstraat 6, 2584 AM, The Hague, Netherlands.

NORWAY

The Royal Norwegian Ministry of Church and Education and **The Royal Ministry of Cultural and Scientific Affairs,**
Dep. Oslo 1, Norway.
Academic calendar runs from September to June. Primary language of instruction is Norwegian; other language of instruction is Lappish in the northern region.
The Ministry reports that any foreign teacher desiring a permanent position in a Norwegian school must pass an examination, administered by the National Council for Teachers Training, on Norwegian language and civilization. Foreign teachers interested in obtaining positions in a teachers training college or university should apply directly to the particular institution. Vacancies are advertised in *Norsk Lysingsblad*. Subscriptions are available for 156 Norwegian kroner from Akerist 34, Oslo 1, Norway. Information about temporary and part-time positions is available from some of the voluntary adult educational organizations in Norway. Two such organizations are Studentersamfundets Friundervisning, Nedre Vollgt. 20, Oslo 1, and Abeidernes Opplysningsforbund, Storgt. 23d, Oslo 1.
Generally, however, it is extremely difficult for foreign teachers to obtain positions in Norway. Since 1975, there has been a ban on immigration, and in most cases, work permits, necessary to enter Norway, have been denied.

Stavanger American School,
Treskeveien 3, 4040 Madla, Norway.
This private, coed primary/secondary institution, also offering adult-education courses, was founded in 1966. Academic calendar runs from late August to mid-June. Primary language of instruction is English; other languages of instruction are Norwegian, Spanish and French. Current enrollment is 420; 100 percent of faculty are U.S. nationals. Curriculum is parallel to that of a U.S. private school.
Opportunities: Ten to 15 positions annually for teachers of grades one through six in reading, physical education, music and art. Positions for secondary-level teachers in all subjects. Positions for vocational (secondary-level) teachers in typing, shop, mechanical drawing, and photography. Positions for library administrators and counselors also available.
Requirements: U.S. bachelor's degree in appropriate field is required; U.S. master's degree is preferred; U.S. Ph.D. degree in science, mathematics is preferred. Two to ten

years' teaching experience is required. Preference to single applicants or married teaching couples; applicants with more than one child are not usually considered.
Duration: One year; renewable.
Benefits: Salary ranges from $14,000–$35,000 for administrators (tax free). Three-day pre-assignment orientation in Norway. Transportation is included for appointee and dependents. Housing is not included; housing allowances are provided. Dependent child receives free tuition. Comprehensive Norwegian national insurance program and cost of living allowances are provided.
Application: December 1 for following August 15; notification in April.
Contact: Mr. Miles H. Lovelace, Superintendent, Stavanger American School, Treskeveien 3, 4040 Madla, Norway.

POLAND

Embassy of the Polish People's Republic,
2640 16th St. NW, Washington, DC 20009.
Academic calendar runs from early October to mid-June. Primary language of instruction is Polish.
The Embassy reports that there is no need for U.S. teachers, educational administrators, or teachers of English as a second/foreign language at the present time.

American School of Warsaw,
Warsaw, Dept. of State, Washington, DC 20520.
This private, coed primary-level institution was founded in 1953. Academic calendar runs from September to June. Primary language of instruction is English; other languages of instruction are French and Polish as foreign languages. Current enrollment is 175; 86 percent of faculty are non-native; 66 percent of faculty are U.S. nationals.
Opportunities: Two to four positions annually for teachers of self-contained classes (grades kindergarten through eight); and mathematics, science, language arts, and social studies teachers (grades seven through eight). Two positions for teachers of English as a second language.
Requirements: U.S. bachelor's degree in elementary education is required; U.S. master's degree is preferred. Two years' teaching experience is required. Previous international experience is preferred.
Duration: Two years; renewable for two-year intervals.
Benefits: Salary is $11,255–$21,363, based upon degree and experience. Transportation is included for appointee and dependents up to age 13. Housing is included. Home leave is included after two years. Blue Cross/Blue Shield is provided for appointee and dependents.
Application: Mid-February; notification in early April.
Contact: Director, American School of Warsaw, Warsaw, Dept. of State, Washington, DC 20520.

PORTUGAL

American International School of Lisbon,
Quinta Casa Branca, Carnaxide, Portugal.
This is a private, coed primary/secondary institution. Academic calendar runs from September to June. Primary language of instruction is English; secondary language of instruction is Portuguese; other language of instruction is French. Current enrollment is 270; 89 percent of faculty are non-native; 83 percent of faculty are U.S. nationals.
There is no formal employment program for hiring U.S. educators. Listed is general information on faculty recruitment.
Opportunities: Eight to ten positions, including one or two for teachers of English as a second/foreign language on the secondary level.

Requirements: U.S. bachelor's degree is required; U.S. master's degree is preferred. Portuguese language proficiency is preferred. Previous international experience is required.

For *TESL/TEFL:* U.S. master's degree in applied linguistics is required. Portuguese language proficiency is preferred. Two years' teaching experience is required. Previous international experience is preferred.

Duration: Two years; renewable for one year.

Benefits: Salary varies with experience and training. Two-week pre-assignment orientation in Portugal. Transportation is included for appointee and two dependents. Housing is included. Local medical plan and life insurance are provided. Moving and shipping allowance is included, as well as an allowance for professional books.

Application: January for following year; notification by March.

Contact: American International School of Lisbon, Apartado 10, Carnaxide 2795 Linda-a-Velha, Portugal.

ROMANIA

U.S. Information Service,
American Embassy—Bucharest, APO NY 09213.

Opportunities: *Fulbright-Hays Program.* Ten positions annually for teachers of agriculture, business, mathematics, American literature, and English as a foreign language on the university level. Up to seven research awards for three to 10 months are also available.

Requirements: U.S. Ph.D. degree in appropriate field is required. Romanian language proficiency is preferred. Previous teaching experience is required. Previous international experience is preferred.

For *TESL/TEFL:* U.S. master's degree in applied linguistics is required; U.S. Ph.D. degree in applied linguistics is preferred. Romanian language proficiency is preferred. Previous teaching experience is required.

Duration: Ten to 20 months; not renewable.

Benefits: Salary is $16,000–$24,000. Three-day pre-assignment orientation in Washington, DC. Transportation is included for appointee only. Housing is included. Dependent children may attend American School in Bucharest.

Application: September 15; notification by late June to August.

Contact: Council for International Exchange of Scholars, 11 Dupont Circle, Washington, DC 20036.

SPAIN

Ministerio de Educación y Ciencia,
Cartegena 83-85, Madrid.

Academic calendar runs from September to May/June. Primary languages of instruction are Spanish and regional languages; other languages of instruction are English, French, and German in international schools.

The Ministry reports that U.S. teachers and teachers of English as a second language are employed at commercial language academies and for primary/secondary level at private international schools.

Contact: U.S. Information Agency, Washington, DC 20547, or Commission for Educational Exchange between the U.S. and Spain, C/Cartagena, 83–85, 3a planta, Madrid 28, Spain.

Commission for Educational Exchange between the U.S. and Spain,
C/Cartagena 83-85, 3a planta., Madrid 28, Spain.

Opportunities: *Fulbright-Hays Program.* Three positions annually for lecturers in American studies at one of three Spanish universities. Primary concentration is on American literature.

Requirements: U.S. Ph.D. degree is required, although advanced Ph.D. candidates will be considered.
Duration: Nine months.
Contact: Council for International Exchange of Scholars, 11 Dupont Circle, Washington, DC 20036.

American School of Barcelona,
Pasaje Font del Lleo, S/M Barcelona 34, Spain.
This private, coed primary/secondary institution was founded in 1962. Academic calendar runs from September to June. Primary language of instruction is English; secondary languages of instruction are Spanish and Catalan. Current enrollment is 400; 70 percent of faculty are non-native; 50 percent of faculty are U.S. nationals.
Opportunities: Two to five positions annually for teachers of kindergarten, mathematics, and sciences.
Requirements: U.S. bachelor's degree in education is required. Spanish language proficiency on the beginning level is preferred. Two years' teaching experience is preferred. Previous international experience is preferred.
Duration: Two years; renewable.
Benefits: Salary is $7,000–$8,000 per year. Transportation is included for appointee only. Housing is not included; approximate cost of housing is $150 per month. Dependent children receive full scholarship. National health plan is provided. Occasional conference opportunities are available.
Application: No deadline; hiring usually done in February; notification by June.
Contact: Director, American School of Barcelona, Pasaje Font del Lleo, S/M Barcelona 34, Spain.

American School of Madrid,
Crta. Humera, Km. 2, Aravaca, Madrid, Spain.
This private, coed primary/secondary institution was founded in 1961. Academic calendar runs from September to June. Primary language of instruction is English; secondary language of instruction is Spanish. Current enrollment is 700; 50 percent of faculty are U.S. nationals.
There is no formal employment program for hiring U.S. educators. Listed is general information on faculty recruitment.
Requirements: U.S. bachelor's degree is required; U.S. master's or Ph.D. degree is preferred. Spanish language proficiency on the intermediate level is preferred. Two years' teaching experience is required. Previous international experience is preferred.
Duration: Two years; renewable for one year.
Benefits: Salary is based upon experience, according to a set scale. Transportation is included for appointee and dependents. Housing is not included; approximate cost of housing is 35,000 pesetas per month. Free tuition for dependent children is available. Blue Cross/Blue Shield and life insurance are provided; social security is included. Overseas allowance of 100,000 pesetas for first year.
Application: Spring.
Contact: American School of Madrid, Crta. Humera, Km. 2, Aravaca, Madrid, Spain.

American School of Mallorca,
Calle Oratorio 9, Portals Nous, Mallorca, Spain.
This public, coed primary/secondary, special-education institution was founded in 1969. Academic calendar runs from September to June. Primary language of instruction is English. Current enrollment is 180; 95 percent of faculty are non-native; 80 percent of faculty are U.S. nationals.
Opportunities: Positions annually for teachers of various fields of study on primary/secondary level.
Requirements: U.S. bachelor's degree is required; U.S. master's degree is preferred. Spanish language proficiency on the intermediate level is preferred. Two years' teaching experience is required.
Duration: Varies.
Benefits: Salary varies. Transportation is included for appointee only. Housing is not included; approximate cost of housing is $150 per month. An educational allowance is provided for dependent children.

Application: No deadline.
Contact: The Headmaster, American School of Mallorca, Calle Oratorio 9, Portals Nous, Mallorca, Spain.

Baleares International School,
Calle Cabo Mateu Coch, 17, Palma de Mallorca, Spain.
This private, coed primary/secondary institution was founded in 1957. Academic calendar runs from September to June. Primary language of instruction is English; other languages of instruction are Spanish, French and German. Current enrollment is 180; 90 percent of faculty are non-native; 5 percent of faculty are U.S. nationals.
Opportunities: One to two positions every two years. Very little staff movement. Recruitment is primarily local. Extremely important that teachers fit the Spanish *ambiente* and can teach in other areas.
Requirements: U.S. bachelor's degree in education or subject field is required; U.S. master's degree is preferred. Spanish language proficiency is preferred. Two years' teaching experience is preferred.
Duration: Average seven years; contract becomes permanent after one year.
Benefits: Salary is based upon Spanish government scales; about one-half U.S. salary in middle range. Three-day pre-assignment orientation at school. Transportation is included for appointee only; there may be restrictions. Housing is not included; however, a housing allowance is provided. Free tuition for dependent children is available. Home leave is included every two years. School pays 95 percent of state insurance.
Application: Open.
Contact: The Directors, Baleares International School, Calle Cabo Mateu Coch, 17, Palma de Mallorca, Spain.

Center for Cross-Cultural Study,
Plaza San Francisco, 3, Sevilla, Spain.
This private, coed vocational- and university-level institution was founded in 1971. Academic calendar runs from September to July. Primary languages of instruction are Spanish to U.S. students, English to Spanish students. Current enrollment is 150; 50 percent of faculty are non-native; 50 percent of faculty are U.S. nationals.
Opportunities: Three positions annually for teachers of English as a foreign language. A resident director for American college program needed every two years; assistant director and counselor needed at alternate two-year intervals.
Requirements: U.S. bachelor's degree in Spanish is required for assistant director; U.S. Ph.D. degree in Spanish or Intercultural Communications is required for director (master's degree plus work toward a doctorate is acceptable). Spanish language proficiency on the advanced level is required. Four years' teaching experience is required for director. One year's international experience in Spain is required for assistant. Previous international experience is also required for director.
For *TESL/TEFL:* U.S. bachelor's degree in linguistics or teaching English as a second/foreign language is required; U.S. master's degree in applied linguistics or teaching English as a second/foreign language is preferred. Spanish language proficiency on the intermediate level is preferred. Two years' teaching experience is preferred. Previous international experience within a Spanish-speaking country is preferred.
Duration: Two years; not renewable for director/assistant. One year; renewable for TESL/TEFL.
Benefits: Salary is about $14,000 for director; 500.000 pesetas plus $1,200 for assistant; 600.000 pesetas plus health insurance and one-month vacation for TESL/TEFL. Transportation is included for director only. Housing is included. Dependents receive free tuition at Center for Cross-Cultural Study and University of Seville. Resident director and assistant receive Spanish social security.
Application: February 1; notification by late Spring/early Summer.
Contact: Dr. Gerald Guidera, Director of the Center, Center for Cross-Cultural Study, 31 Maplewood Dr., Amherst, MA 01002.

SWEDEN

Commission for Educational Exchange between the U.S. and Sweden,
Norrmalmstorg 1, 111 46 Stockholm, Sweden.

The Fulbright Commission reports that due to difficulties in the labor market and a surplus of qualified teachers, the Swedish Fulbright Commission no longer brings U.S. teachers to Sweden. U.S. teachers should contact the National Labour Market Board, Section for Foreigners, S-171 99 Solna, Sweden, for possible opportunities or write directly to the few English-speaking schools located in Sweden.

National Swedish Board of Education,
S-106, 42, Stockholm, Sweden.

Academic calendar runs from late August to mid-June. Primary language of instruction is Swedish; secondary language of instruction is English; other languages of instruction are French and German.

The Ministry reports that there is no need for U.S. teachers, educational administrators, or teachers of English as a second/foreign language at the present time.

SWITZERLAND

Embassy of Switzerland,
2900 Cathedral Ave. NW, Washington, DC 20008.

Association Suisse des Professeurs D'Universite,
Sophienstrasse 2, 8032 Zurich, Switzerland.

Academic calendar runs from October to July. Primary languages of instruction are German and French.

The Ministry and Embassy report that foreign citizens are prohibited to teach in the Swiss public school system, unless they are placed through the *U.S.-Swiss Teacher Exchange* administered by the U.S. Department of Education (see page 6). A very limited number of foreign teachers may find positions in Swiss private schools, provided that a working permit can be obtained.

American International School of Zurich,
Nidelbadstrasse 49, 8802 Kilchberg, Switzerland.

This is a private, coed secondary-level institution. Academic calendar runs from September to June. Primary language of instruction is English. Current enrollment is 200; 60 percent of faculty are U.S. nationals.

Opportunities: One position every five years for science, mathematics, and computer science teacher. All teaching positions are subject to strict work permit quotas. Direct application is discouraged. Recruitment is done through the European Council of Independent Schools.

Requirements: U.S. bachelor's degree is required; U.S. master's degree is preferred. German language proficiency on the intermediate level is preferred. Five years' teaching experience is required. Previous international experience is preferred.

For *TESL/TEFL:* U.S. bachelor's degree in English is required; U.S. master's degree is preferred. German language proficiency on the intermediate level is preferred. Five years' teaching experience is required. Previous international experience is preferred.

Duration: One year; renewable annually.

Benefits: Salary is based upon background and experience and paid in Swiss francs. Transportation is not included. Housing is not included; approximate cost of housing is 1,400 SFR per month.

Foundation of the International School of Geneva,
62 rte de Cheñe, 1208 Geneva, Switzerland.

This private, coed primary/secondary institution, with facilities for special education and offering adult-education courses, was founded in 1924. Academic calendar runs from September to June. Primary language of instruction is English; secondary language of instruction is French. Current enrollment is 2,500; 80 percent of faculty are non-native; 12 percent of faculty are U.S. nationals.

Opportunities: Three to four positions annually for teachers of all subject areas on the secondary level and one to two positions for teachers of English as a second/foreign language.

Requirements: U.S. master's degree is preferred. Three years' teaching experience is preferred. Previous international experience is preferred.

For *TESL/TEFL:* U.S. master's degree in linguistics is preferred.

Duration: Two years; renewable.

Benefits: Salary is 42,000–66,000 Swiss francs. Transportation is included for appointee and dependents. Housing is not included; approximate cost of housing is 1,200 SFR per month. Home leave is included. Educational allowances and medical insurance are provided.

Application: March 1; notification in April.

Contact: Director General, Foundation for the International School of Geneva, 62 rte de Cheñe, 1208 Geneva, Switzerland.

Institut Montana,
6316 Zugerberg, Zug, Switzerland.

This private, male only, primary/secondary institution was founded in 1952. Academic calendar runs from September to June. Primary language of instruction is English; other languages of instruction are French and German. Current enrollment is 55; 50 percent of faculty are U.S. nationals.

Opportunities: Generally one to two positions annually for English, mathematics, social studies, and science teachers on the primary level, and same plus French, German, music, and art on the secondary level. Occasionally there is need for a teacher of English as a foreign language.

Requirements: U.S. bachelor's degree in appropriate field is required; U.S. master's degree is preferred. One to two years' teaching experience is preferred. Candidates must be unmarried.

For *TESL/TEFL:* U.S. bachelor's degree in linguistics or applied linguistics is required; U.S. master's degree is preferred. Previous teaching experience is preferred.

Duration: Two years; renewable.

Benefits: Salary is 1,500 Swiss francs per month for 12 months. Transportation is not included. Housing is included with meals, utilities, maid and laundry services. Accident and health insurance are provided.

Application: Early spring.

Contact: Peter H. Oehrlein, Dean of the American School, Institut Montana, 6316 Zugerberg, Zug, Switzerland.

International School of Basel,
P.O. Box 319, 4103 Bottmingen, Switzerland.

This private, coed primary-level institution was founded in 1979. Academic calendar runs from September to June. Primary language of instruction is English; secondary languages of instruction are German and French. Current enrollment is 85; 90 percent of faculty are non-native; 25 percent of faculty are U.S. nationals.

There is no formal employment program for hiring U.S. educators. Listed is general information on faculty recruitment.

Requirements: U.S. bachelor's degree is required. Two years' teaching experience is required. Previous international experience is preferred.

For *TESL/TEFL:* U.S. bachelor's degree in teaching English as a second/foreign language is required. Previous teaching experience is preferred.

Duration: One to two years; renewable.

Benefits: Salary is 30,000 Swiss francs ($15,000) per year. For TESL/TEFL; 30 Swiss francs per hour. One-week pre-assignment orientation at school. Transportation is not included. Housing is not included; approximate cost of housing is 300 SFR per month. Educational allowances are provided on individual basis. Accident insurance is provided; pension plan will be available beginning 1985.

Application: March/April.

Contact: Janet Galli, Director, International School of Basel, P.O. Box 319, 4103 Bottmingen, Switzerland.

International School of Berne,
Mattenstr. 3, 3073 Gümligen, Switzerland.
This private, coed primary/secondary institution was founded in 1961. Academic calendar runs from September to June. Primary language of instruction is English; other languages of instruction are German and French. Current enrollment is 145; 95 percent of faculty are non-native; 60 percent of faculty are U.S. nationals.
Opportunities: About three positions annually.
Requirements: U.S. bachelor's degree is required; U.S. master's degree is preferred. Two years' teaching experience is required. Previous international experience is preferred.
Duration: One year; renewable.
Benefits: Salary is about $17,000. Transportation is not included. Housing is not included. Medical insurance and pension plan are provided.
Application: Open; notification by May 30.
Contact: Dr. Keith Costello, Headmaster, International School of Berne, Mattenstr. 3, 3073 Gümligen, Switzerland.

UNION OF SOVIET SOCIALIST REPUBLICS

Anglo-American School—Moscow,
American Embassy, Moscow, APO NY 09862.
This private, coed primary/secondary institution was founded in 1949. Academic calendar runs from September to June. Primary language of instruction is English; other languages of instruction are Russian and French. Current enrollment is 275; 50 percent of faculty are U.S. nationals.
Opportunities: About eight positions annually for mathematics, science, computer, music, and physical education teachers on the secondary level, and one position for a teacher of English as a second language.
Requirements: U.S. bachelor's degree in liberal arts is required; U.S. master's degree in education is preferred. Russian language proficiency is preferred. Two years' teaching experience is required. Previous international experience is preferred.
For *TESL/TEFL:* U.S. master's degree in English as a second language or applied linguistics is preferred. Russian language proficiency is preferred. Two years' teaching experience is required.
Duration: Two years; renewable.
Benefits: Salary is $13,000–$18,000 per year. Transportation is included for appointee and dependents. Housing is included. Home leave is included after two years.
Application: February; notification by spring.
Contact: James Ruckhert, Director, Anglo-American School—Moscow, American Embassy, Moscow APO NY 09862.

UNITED KINGDOM

British Information Services,
845 Third Ave., New York, NY 10022.
Academic calendar runs from October to June. Primary language of instruction is English.
Vacancies for teaching positions are advertised in *The Times Education Supplement, The Times Higher Education Supplement, The Teacher,* and *Scottish Education Journal.* Foreign employees must possess a work permit issued by the British Department of Employment. Presently, opportunities are scarce for foreign teachers in Britain, and work permits are only issued for teachers of mathematics and/or the natural sciences.
In Britain, each local Education Authority appoints teachers to the schools for which they are responsible. Applications should be directed to the appropriate Authority.

Authority addresses can be found in *The Education Authorities Directory and Annual 1980.* British Information Services will only supply two Authority addresses by mail.

Applications for employment at independent (private) schools should be made directly to the school. A placement service is provided by the European Council of International Schools, Inc., 19 Claremont Rd., Surbiton, Surrey KT6 4QR, England, for vacancies chiefly in schools affiliated with the Council.

There is an annual exchange of teachers between the United States and the United Kingdom (see page 80).

Allington Manor International Special School,

Allington Manor, Fair Oak, Hants. SO5 7DE, United Kingdom.

This private, coed special-education institution was founded in 1977. Academic calendar runs from January to July, March to September, or April to December. Primary language of instruction is English. Current enrollment is 25. Teacher student ratio is 1:2.5.

Opportunities: *Special and Remedial Education.* About three positions for teachers of all subjects on primary/secondary level. Note: students enrolled in this program have IQ's ranging from 80 to 135 on the WISC test. Special emphasis on experience with emotional and behavioral problems in children.

Requirements: U.S. bachelor's degree is preferred. Two years' teaching experience is preferred. Experience and dedication are more important than academic credentials.

Duration: One to three years; renewable.

Benefits: Salary is based upon experience. Pre-assignment orientation. Transportation is not included. Housing is included. Medical insurance is provided.

Application: Open.

Contact: Dr. L. F. Lowenstein, Director, Allington Manor International Special School, Allington Manor, Fair Oak, Hants. SO5 7DE, United Kingdom.

American College in London,

100 Marylebone Lane, London W1M 5FP, United Kingdom.

This private, coed university was founded in 1970. Academic calendar runs from September to May. Primary language of instruction is English. Current enrollment is 325; 55 percent of faculty are non-native; 45 percent of faculty are U.S. nationals.

There is no formal employment program for hiring U.S. educators. Listed is general information on faculty recruitment.

Opportunities: Three to four positions for teachers of business administration, fashion merchandising, design, and interior design.

Requirements: U.S. bachelor's degree in appropriate field is required; U.S. master's degree is preferred. Three to five years' teaching experience is preferred. Previous international experience is preferred. The philosophy of the college is to hire professionals rather than professional educators.

Duration: Varies.

Benefits: Salary begins at £9,500 per year. Transportation is usually included for appointee only. Housing is not included; approximate cost of housing is £75 per week and up. Full-time employees covered under the National Health Service.

Application: Open.

Contact: The President, American College in London, 100 Marylebone Lane, London W1M 5FP, United Kingdom.

American Community Schools,

Portsmouth Rd., Cobham, Surrey, United Kingdom.

These private, coed institutions were founded in 1967. There are two American schools, serving grades nursery through 13, and one Dutch school, serving grades kindergarten through six. Academic calendar runs from late August to late June. Primary language of instruction is English in the American School, Dutch in the Dutch school; other languages of instruction are French, German, and Spanish. Current enrollment is 1,200; 70 percent of faculty are U.S. nationals.

One of the schools follows traditional U.S. curriculum, the second school offers the international baccalaureate, and the third follows the Dutch curriculum.

An information pamphlet on living and working in the United Kingdom is sent to prospective teachers with the employment application.

Opportunities: About 25 positions annually for primary- and secondary-level teachers. Special need for mathematics and science teachers (secondary level) and teachers of remedial reading, and the learning disabled (grades kindergarten through eight). In addition, two English-as-a-second-language teachers are needed.

Requirements: U.S. bachelor's degree is required; U.S. master's degree in education is preferred. Two years' recent teaching experience is required.

For *TESL/TEFL:* U.S. bachelor's degree in teaching English as a second language is required. Two years' teaching experience is required.

Duration: Two years; renewable.

Benefits: Salary is £9,100–12,000. Transportation is included up to £500. Housing is not included; approximate cost of housing is 25 to 30 percent of annual income. Free tuition for dependent children is available; teachers receive maximum £250 for approved courses. Medical and life insurance are provided.

Application: March to June.

Contact: Personnel Officer, American Community Schools, Portsmouth Rd., Cobham, Surrey, United Kingdom.

American School in Aberdeen Educational Trust Ltd.,
Craigton Rd., Cults, Aberdeen AB1 9QD, Scotland, United Kingdom.

This private, coed primary/secondary institution was founded in 1972. Academic calendar runs from August to June. Primary language of instruction is English; other languages of instruction are Spanish and French. Current enrollment is 310; 80 percent of faculty are U.S. nationals. This is an oil companies' school, established primarily for educating the children of U.S. employees.

Opportunities: About five positions annually.

Requirements: U.S. bachelor's degree in education is required; U.S. master's or Ph.D. degree in specific subject area is preferred. Two years' teaching experience is required. Previous international experience is preferred.

Duration: Two years; renewable annually.

Benefits: Salary is based upon education and experience. One-week pre-assignment orientation at school. Transportation is included for appointee and dependents. Housing supplement is included; approximate cost of housing is £200–£300 per month. Home leave is provided. National health insurance and $25,000 life insurance policy are provided. Storage allowance of $625 per year and 25 percent overseas living allowance is included.

Application: February 1; notification by March.

Contact: Everett G. Gould, Superintendent/Headmaster, American School in Aberdeen Educational Trust Ltd., Craigton Rd., Cults, Aberdeen AB1 9QD, Scotland, United Kingdom.

American School in London,
2-8 Loudoun Rd., London NW8 0NP, United Kingdom.

This private, coed primary/secondary institution was founded in 1951. Academic calendar runs from September to June. Primary language of instruction is English. Current enrollment is 1,450; 85 percent of faculty are non-native; 84 percent of faculty are U.S. nationals.

Opportunities: Five to ten positions annually; two to three positions are arranged as a formal exchange with private/public schools.

Requirements: U.S. bachelor's degree is required; U.S. master's degree is preferred. Two years' teaching experience is required.

Duration: Two years; renewable.

Benefits: Salary is £9,993–£19,505 based upon experience and education. Transportation is included for appointee and dependents. Housing is not included; approximate cost of housing is £50–£100 per week. Dependent children qualify for free tuition. Medical, life, and disability insurance is provided. About £200 per year available for courses and conferences.

Application: February 1; notification by late March.

Contact: Headmaster, American School in London, 2-8 Loudoun Rd., London NW8 0NP, United Kingdom.

Brown and Brown and Tutors,
20 Warnborough Rd., Oxford, United Kingdom.

This private, secondary-level organization, founded in 1971, offers private tutoring for U.S. and British students. Academic calendar runs from September to September. Primary language of instruction is English; secondary language of instruction is French. Current enrollment is 120; 12 percent of faculty are non-native; eight percent of faculty are U.S. nationals.

Opportunities: One position for an American history teacher and one for a coordinator of the Advanced Placement Summer Program.

Requirements: U.S. master's degree in U.S. history is required. French language proficiency on the beginning level is preferred. Five years' teaching experience is required. Previous international experience is preferred.

Duration: Two months to one year; renewable as required.

Benefits: Salary is £5.25 per hour. Three-week pre-assignment orientation in Oxford. Transportation is not included. Housing is not included; approximate cost of housing is £30 per week.

Application: July for September acceptance.

Contact: Principal, Brown and Brown and Tutors, Warnborough Rd., Oxford, United Kingdom.

Central Bureau for Educational Visits and Exchanges,
Seymour Mews House, Seymour Mews, London W1H 9PE, United Kingdom.

This foreign-based organization founded in 1948 serves teachers, lecturers, and administrators.

Opportunities: *Teacher Exchange.* About 200 positions annually for teachers of all subject areas on all academic levels.

Requirements: U.S. bachelor's degree in education is required; teacher certification is required. Three years' teaching experience is required. Previous international experience is preferred.

Duration: One year; renewable for one year.

Benefits: Teachers retain own salary. One-day pre-assignment orientation in United States. Transportation is not included. Housing is not included. Children attend British schools. Participants are covered by National Health Service; $2,000 per incident health insurance provided.

Application: October 15; notification by March.

Contact: Teacher Exchange Branch, U.S. Department of Education, International Education Programs, Washington, DC 20202.

Hampstead International School,
16 Netherhall Gardens, London NW3 5TJ, United Kingdom.

This private, coed institution offering primary-level special education was founded in 1967. Academic calendar runs from September to June. Primary language of instruction is English. Current enrollment is 110; 60 percent of faculty are U.S. nationals.

Opportunities: Three to four positions annually for primary education teachers and two positions for teachers of English as a foreign language.

Requirements: U.S. bachelor's degree in elementary education is required; U.S. master's degree is preferred. Two or more years' teaching experience is required. Previous international experience is preferred.

For *TESL/TEFL:* U.S. bachelor's degree in elementary education is required; U.S. graduate courses in English as a second language are preferred. Two or more years teaching experience is required. Previous international experience is preferred.

Duration: Two years; renewable for two years.

Benefits: Salary is based upon experience. One-day pre-assignment orientation at the school. Transportation is not included. Housing is not included; approximate cost of a one-bedroom flat is £50 per week. Appointees are covered under the National Health Service.

Application: April 1.

Contact: Mrs. E. Murphy, Hampstead International School, 16 Netherhall Gardens, London NW3 5TJ, United Kingdom.

TASIS England American School,
Coldharbour Lane, Thorpe, Surrey, TW20 8TE, United Kingdom.
This private, coed primary/secondary institution was founded in 1976. Academic calendar runs from September to June. Primary language of instruction is English. Current enrollment is 487; 90 percent of faculty are U.S. nationals.

Opportunities: About 20 positions annually for teachers of grades kindergarten through six; also positions for teachers of mathematics, science, history, and foreign language (French, Spanish, and German) on the secondary level. In addition, there are two full-time and eight summer positions for teachers of English as a foreign language.

Requirements: U.S. bachelor's degree is required; U.S. master's degree is preferred. Two years' teaching experience is required.
For *TESL/TEFL:* U.S. bachelor's or master's degree in applied linguistics is preferred. Two years' teaching experience is required.

Duration: Two years; renewable on an individual basis annually.

Benefits: Salary is £5,000–£8,000 per academic year. One-week pre-assignment orientation in England. Transportation is not included; one-time travel allowance of $300 is given. Housing is included for 40 percent of staff; approximate cost of housing is $250 per month. Dependent children receive free tuition. Appointees are covered by National Health Service.

Application: Open.

Contact: Mr. DeHaven W. Fleming, Headmaster, TASIS England American School, Coldharbour Lane, Thorpe, Surrey TW20 8TE, United Kingdom.

WESTERN
HEMISPHERE

ARGENTINA

Embassy of Argentina,
1600 New Hampshire Ave. NW, Washington, DC 20009.
Academic calendar runs from March to November. Primary language of instruction is Spanish.
The Embassy reports that there is no need for U.S. teachers, educational administrators, or teachers of English as a second/foreign language at the present time.

Lincoln—The American Community School,
Andres Ferreyra 4073, 1636 La Lucila, Buenos Aires, Argentina.
This private, coed primary/secondary institution, with limited facilities for special education, was founded in 1952. Academic calendar runs from August to December and February to June. Primary language of instruction is English (for grades kindergarten through 12); secondary language of instruction is Spanish (for grades kindergarten through seven). Current enrollment is 550; 20 percent of faculty are U.S. nationals.
Opportunities: One to two positions as needed. Faculty is international, with most obtaining their education in the United States or Argentina, and the majority hold advanced degrees. Counselors are also employed in both the elementary and secondary school. Teachers of English as a second/foreign language are hired locally.
Requirements: U.S. bachelor's degree is required. U.S. master's or Ph.D. degree is preferred. Previous teaching experience is required. Previous international experience is preferred. Teaching certification is required.
Benefits: Salary is $18,000–$30,000. Housing is included. Annual home leave is included. Medical insurance is provided.
Application: Open.
Contact: Ralph A. Rubano, Superintendent, Lincoln—The American Community School, Andres Ferreyra 4073, 1636 La Lucila, Buenos Aires, Argentina.

BARBADOS

Ministry of Education,
Jemmott's Lane, St. Michael, Barbados, West Indies.
Academic calendar runs from September to August. Primary language of instruction is English.
The Ministry reports that there is no need for U.S. teachers, educational administrators, or teachers of English as a second/foreign language at the present time.

BELIZE

Ministry of Education,
Belmopan, Belize.
Academic calendar runs from September to June. Primary language of instruction is English.
The Ministry reports that there is no need for U.S. teachers, educational administrators or teachers of English as a second/foreign language at the present time.

BOLIVIA

American Cooperative School,
c/o American Embassy, La Paz, Bolivia.
This private, coed primary/secondary institution was founded in 1955. Academic calendar runs from mid-August to late May. Primary language of instruction is English; other language of instruction is Spanish. Current enrollment is 469; 80 percent of faculty are U.S. nationals.

Opportunities: About eight positions annually for mathematics and science teachers on the secondary level. Also positions for general education teachers and teachers of English as a second language.

Requirements: U.S. bachelor's degree is required. Spanish language proficiency on the beginning level is preferred. Two years' teaching experience is preferred. Previous international experience is preferred.

For *TESL/TEFL:* U.S. bachelor's degree in applied linguistics is preferred. Spanish language proficiency is preferred. Two years' teaching experience is preferred. Previous international experience is preferred.

Duration: Two years; renewable for one year.

Benefits: Salary is $9,000–$14,000. Transportation is included for appointee and dependents. Housing is included. Free tuition for dependent children is available. Blue Cross is provided.

Application: Not given; notification by April.

Contact: Herman J. Penland, Superintendent, American Cooperative School, c/o U.S. Embassy, La Paz, Bolivia.

Centro Boliviano Americano,
P.O. Box 1399, Cochabamba, Bolivia.

This foreign-based organization founded in 1957 serves South American teachers, lecturers, TESL/TEFL, and guidance counselors.

Duration: Two years; renewable for two years.

Benefits: Salary is above average scale. Two-week pre-assignment orientation in Cochabamba. Transportation is not included. Housing is not included; approximate cost of housing is Bolivian $10,000 per month. Medical insurance is provided.

Application: No deadline.

Contact: Enrique Huerta, Executive Director, Centro Boliviano Americano, P.O. Box 1399, Cochabamba, Bolivia.

Centro Boliviano Americano,
Casilla 20623, La Paz, Bolivia.

This foreign-based organization founded in 1938 serves Bolivian teachers, lecturers, TESL/TEFL, administrators, and guidance counselors.

Opportunities: *English Teaching Fellow.* One position annually for a teacher of English as a second/foreign language on the adult/extension-education level.

Requirements: U.S. master's degree in English as a second language is preferred. Spanish language proficiency on the intermediate level is preferred. Two years' teaching experience is required. Previous international experience is preferred.

Duration: Two years; not renewable.

Benefits: Salary is $700 per month. Two-week pre-assignment orientation in La Paz. Transportation is included for appointee only. Housing is not included; approximate cost of housing is $100 per month. General medical insurance is provided. Two months' extra salary and a $1,000 yearly bonus given.

Application: Not given.

Contact: U.S. Information Agency, 400 C St. SW, Washington, DC 20547, or Centro Boliviano Americano, Casilla 20623, La Paz, Bolivia.

Cochabamba Cooperative School,
Casilla 1395, Cochabamba, Bolivia.

This private, coed primary/secondary institution was founded in 1954. Academic calendar runs from August to June. Primary language of instruction is English; other languages of instruction are Spanish, French, and German. Current enrollment is 356; 19 percent of faculty are non-native; 38 percent of faculty are U.S. nationals.

Opportunities: Two positions for teachers of grades two through six and mathematics, social studies, and English teachers on the secondary level. Also one position available for teacher of intensive English.

Requirements: U.S. bachelor's degree is required; U.S. master's degree is preferred. Spanish language proficiency on the intermediate level is preferred. Two years' teaching experience is required. Previous international experience is preferred.

For *TESL/TEFL:* U.S. bachelor's degree in applied linguistics is preferred. Spanish language proficiency on the intermediate level is preferred. Two years' teaching experience is required.

Duration: Two years; renewable annually.

Benefits: Salary is $7,500–$12,000, payable half in pesos and half in U.S. dollars. Transportation is included for appointee and dependents. Housing is included. Blue Cross/Blue Shield is provided.

Application: February 1.

Contact: Director, Cochabamba Cooperative School, Casilla 1395, Cochabamba, Bolivia.

Santa Cruz Cooperative School,

Casilla 753, Santa Cruz, Bolivia.

This private, coed secondary institution was founded in 1959. Academic calendar runs from August to May. Primary language of instruction is English; secondary language of instruction is Spanish. Current enrollment is 385; 85 percent of faculty are non-native; 75 percent of faculty are U.S. nationals.

Opportunities: Positions annually for teachers of social studies, mathematics, science, and English on the secondary level. In addition, 12 positions available for teachers of English as a second language. Faculty is often recruited at "recruitment fairs" in the United States.

Requirements: U.S. bachelor's degree is required; U.S. master's or Ph.D. degree is preferred. Spanish language proficiency on the beginning level is preferred. Two years' teaching experience is preferred. Previous international experience is preferred. Teacher certification in subject area is preferred.

For *TESL/TEFL:* U.S. bachelor's or master's degree in linguistics or English is preferred. Spanish language proficiency on the beginning level is preferred. Two years' teaching experience is preferred. Previous international experience is preferred.

Duration: Two years; renewable.

Benefits: One-week pre-assignment orientation in Bolivia. Transportation is included for appointee and dependents. Housing is included. Blue Cross/Blue Shield is provided.

Application: February.

Contact: Santa Cruz Cooperative School, Casilla 753, Santa Cruz, Bolivia.

BRAZIL

Commission for Educational Exchange between the United States and Brazil,

Avenida Presidente Wilson, 147, Third Floor, Rio de Janeiro, Brazil.

Academic calendar runs from March to November. Primary language of instruction is Portuguese.

The Fulbright Commission reports that there is more of an interest in than a need for U.S. lecturers, teachers of English as a second/foreign language, and researchers in vocational/technical, university, and professional education. It must be noted that there are legal restrictions regarding teaching possibilities for U.S. nationals in Brazil. If the teacher is not sponsored through such auspices as the Fulbright Program, Ford Foundation, U.S. Information Agency, home or host institution, or Brazilian Ministry of Education, a permanent visa, issued only after there is a contract, is required. Increasingly, obtaining a contract requires that the teacher be licensed in Brazil, which entails having one's U.S. diploma(s) recognized in Brazil.

For those wishing to teach English as a second/foreign language, there is the common problem of needing to present a contract to obtain a permanent visa but needing a permanent visa in order to obtain a contract.

American School of Brasilia,

C.P. 1093, Brasilia, Brazil.

This private, coed primary/secondary institution was founded in 1964. Academic calendar runs from August to June. Primary language of instruction is English; secondary language of instruction is Portuguese. Current enrollment is 520; 74 percent of faculty are non-native; 63 percent of faculty are U.S. nationals.

Opportunities: Positions for teachers of general education and English as a second language.
Requirements: U.S. bachelor's degree in education is required; U.S. master's degree in education is preferred. Portuguese language proficiency on the beginning level is preferred. Two years' teaching experience is required. Previous international experience is preferred.
Duration: Two years; renewable for two years.
Benefits: Salary is $11,000–$19,800. Transportation is included for appointee and dependents. Housing is included. Medical insurance and tuition benefits are included.
Application: Open; notification in March.
Contact: Dr. Thomas J. Rushcamp, American School of Brasilia, C.P. 1093, Brasilia, Brazil.

Associação Escola Graduada de São Paulo,
Caixa Postal 7432, 01000 São Paulo, Brazil.
   This private, coed primary/secondary institution was founded in 1920. Academic calendar runs from August to June. Primary language of instruction is English; secondary language of instruction is Portuguese. Current enrollment is 1,020; 11 percent of faculty are non-native; 50 percent of faculty are U.S. nationals.
Opportunities: Ten to 12 positions annually, primarily for secondary-level educators. Teaching couples are preferred. English-as-a-second-language teachers are generally hired locally.
Requirements: U.S. bachelor's degree is required; U.S. master's degree is preferred. Three years' teaching experience is required. Previous international experience is preferred.
   For *TESL/TEFL:* U.S. bachelor's degree in teaching English as a second language is preferred. Previous teaching experience is preferred. Previous international experience is preferred.
Duration: Two years; renewable in one-year increments.
Benefits: Salary is based upon background and education. Two-week pre-assignment orientation in São Paulo. Transportation is included for appointee and two dependents. Housing is included. Home leave is included. Free tuition for two dependent children is available. Blue Cross is provided.
Application: January; notification by March.
Contact: David Housel, Associação Escola Graduada de São Paulo, Caixa Postal 7432, 01000 São Paulo, Brazil.

Casa Thomas Jefferson,
SEP—Sul Entrequadras 706, 906 Brasilia, DF Brazil.
   This adult/extension educational institution was founded in 1963 by the U.S. Information Agency to provide an English-as-a-second-language program and to offer programs on U.S. culture. Academic calendar runs from March to December. Primary language of instruction is Portuguese. Current enrollment is 5,500.
Opportunities: *Study of the U.S.* Four positions annually for teachers of American literature, history, and political and economic systems on the adult-education level. Students range from university students to established professionals. Eight-week survey courses are the norm.
Requirements: U.S. Ph.D. degree in above-mentioned fields is required. Portuguese language proficiency on the beginning level is preferred. Previous teaching experience is required. Previous international experience is preferred. Experience in course design and interaction in intercultural settings is preferred.
Duration: Two months; not renewable.
Benefits: Salary is $2,000 per course plus $50 per diem. Two- to three-day pre-assignment orientation in Brazil. Transportation is included. Housing is included.
Contact: Study of the U.S. Program, Casa Thomas Jefferson, c/o American Embassy, APO Miami 34030.

Escola Americana Do Rio de Janeiro,
Estrada Da Gavea 132, 22451 Rio de Janeiro, Brazil.
   This private, coed primary/secondary institution was founded in 1937. Academic calendar runs from August to June. Primary language of instruction is English; secondary

language of instruction is Portuguese. Current enrollment is 840; 70 percent of faculty is non-native; 25 percent of faculty are U.S. nationals.

Opportunities: Three to five positions for a principal and in-service training teachers on the primary level and a principal and curriculum developers on the secondary level.

Requirements: U.S. master's degree in area of instruction is required. Portuguese language proficiency is preferred. Two years' teaching experience is required. Previous international experience is preferred.

Duration: Two years; renewable.

Benefits: Salary is about $20,000 per year. Two-day pre-assignment orientation at Western Michigan University. Transportation is included for appointee and dependents. Housing is included. Free tuition for dependent children is available. Group health and life insurance are provided. An automobile is provided.

Application: December; notification by February 1.

Contact: Dr. Edsel Erickson, Western Michigan University, Kalamazoo, MI 49008.

Escola Pan Americana de Bahia,

Caixa Postal 231 Salvador, Bahia, Brazil.

This private, coed primary/secondary institution was founded in 1959. Academic calendar runs from August to June. Primary language of instruction is English; secondary language of instruction is Portuguese. Current enrollment is 292; 70 percent of faculty are U.S. nationals.

Opportunities: Three to five openings annually for departmentalized positions in grades one through four, five through eight, and nine through 12.

Requirements: U.S. bachelor's degree in education is required; U.S. master's degree in education is preferred. Three years' teaching experience is required. Previous international experience is preferred.

Duration: Two years; renewable for two years.

Benefits: Salary is $11,000–$14,000 payable in local currency. Two-day pre-assignment orientation on campus. Transportation is included for appointee and dependents. Housing is included. Local Golden Cross (similar to Blue Cross) is provided.

Application: February 1; notification by March.

Contact: Tomm J. Elliott, Headmaster, Escola Pan Americana de Bahia, Caixa Postal 231 Salvador, Bahia, Brazil.

CANADA

Canadian Consulate General,

1251 Avenue of the Americas, New York, NY 10020.

Academic calendar runs from September to May. Primary languages of instruction are English and French.

The Mission reports that there is no need for U.S. teachers, educational administrators, or teachers of English as a second/foreign language at this time.

Canadian Education Association,

252 Bloor St. W., Suite S850, Toronto, Ontario M5S 1V5 Canada.

There are ten provinces and two territories in Canada, and each is responsible for its own educational system. There is no federal office or national ministry of education. Candidates wishing to teach in an elementary or secondary school in Canada should write for information and guidance to the department or ministry of education in the capital city of the province or territory in which they are interested. They will be informed of the requirements for those seeking certification and permanent teaching positions. These requirements usually include copies of diplomas and certificates, college transcripts, and proficiency in English or French. In some provinces, Canadian citizenship is required for permanent certification. Candidates desiring a temporary position only would be well advised to write to the appropriate department of education concerning the requirements and possible opportunities. They should also be warned, however, that temporary opportunities are virtually non-existent.

Great Lakes Christian College,

310 King St. E., Beamsville, Ontario L0R 1B0 Canada.

This private, coed secondary institution/junior college was founded in 1952. Academic calendar runs from September to June. Primary language of instruction is English; other language of instruction is French. Current enrollment is 170; 29 percent of faculty are U.S. nationals.

There is no formal employment program for hiring U.S. educators. Listed is general information on faculty recruitment.

Opportunities: About five positions for mathematics and science teachers on the secondary level.

Requirements: U.S. bachelor's degree in mathematics/science is required; U.S. master's degree in mathematics/science is preferred. Three years' teaching experience is preferred.

Duration: Average is seven years; renewable indefinitely.

Benefits: Salary is $11,300–$21,800. Three-day pre-assignment orientation. Transportation is not included. Housing is not included; approximate cost of housing is Canadian $400 per month. Life insurance, major medical, and indemnity are provided; 30 percent of medical insurance premiums are paid.

Application: March 31.

Contact: Dean, Great Lakes Christian College, Box 399, Beamsville, Ontario L0R 1B0, Canada.

Prairie High School,
c/o Prairie Bible Institute, Three Hills, Alberta T0M 2A0 Canada.

This private, coed secondary-level institution was founded in 1938. Academic calendar runs from September to June. Primary language of instruction is English; secondary language of instruction is French. Current enrollment is 250; 10 percent of faculty are U.S. nationals.

There is no formal employment program for hiring U.S. educators. Listed is general information on faculty recruitment.

Opportunities: Three positions for teachers on the secondary level.

Requirements: U.S. bachelor's degree in appropriate field is required. Previous teaching experience is preferred.

Duration: Open.

Benefits: Salary is based upon economic need rather than credentials; average is $25,000 per year. One-week pre-assignment orientation. Transportation is included. Housing is included. Free tuition for appointees' dependents in Christian schools is available.

Application: Late April.

Contact: R. Brown, Principal, Prairie High School, or Ken Penner, Vice-President of General Education, c/o Prairie Bible Institute, Three Hills, Alberta T0M 2A0 Canada.

CHILE

Ministry of Education (CPEIP),
Casilla 16162, Santiago 9, Chile.

Academic calendar runs from March to January. Primary language of instruction is Spanish.

The Ministry reports that there is no need for U.S. teachers, educational administrators, or teachers of English as a second/foreign language at the present time. Opportunities may, however, be available with private institutions.

Lincoln International Academy,
Casilla 114, Correo 10, Santiago, Chile.

This private, coed primary/secondary institution was founded in 1976. Academic calendar runs from March to December. Primary language of instruction is English; secondary language of instruction is Spanish. Current enrollment is 370; 12.8 percent of faculty are U.S. nationals.

There is no formal employment program for hiring U.S. educators. Listed is general information on faculty recruitment.

Requirements: U.S. bachelor's degree in English is required; U.S. master's degree in English is preferred. Spanish language proficiency on the beginning level is preferred. Two to five years' teaching experience is preferred.
Duration: Three years; renewable.
Benefits: Salary is $500–$1,000 per month. Transportation is not included. Housing is not included; approximate cost of housing is $100 per month.
Application: November.
Contact: Dr. Robert G. Seaquist, Headmaster, Lincoln International Academy, Casilla 114, Correo 10, Santiago, Chile.

Redland School,
Camino El Alba 11357, Las Condes, Santiago, Chile.
    This private, coed primary/secondary institution was founded in 1966. Academic calendar runs from March to December. Primary language of instruction is Spanish; secondary language of instruction is English. Current enrollment is 490; 10 percent of faculty are non-native; two percent of faculty are U.S. nationals.
    There is no formal employment program for hiring U.S. educators. Listed is general information on faculty recruitment.
Requirements: U.S. bachelor's degree in education is preferred. Six years' teaching experience is required. Previous international experience is preferred.
    For *TESL/TEFL:* U.S. bachelor's degree in applied linguistics is preferred. Three years' teaching experience is required. Previous international experience is preferred.
Duration: Three years; renewable for two years.
Benefits: Salary is based upon experience. Transportation is included for appointee only. Housing is not included; the school assists in locating housing.
Contact: Richard Collingwood-Selby, Headmaster, Redland School, Camino El Alba 11357, Las Condes, Santiago, Chile.

Universidad de La Serena,
Casilla 599, La Serena, Chile.
    This private, coed teacher college was founded in 1981 as the result of merging the University of Chile and the State Technical University. Academic calendar runs from March to December. Primary language of instruction is Spanish. Current enrollment is 4,353.
Opportunities: *ESL Teacher-Training Program.* One position annually. This program is currently undergoing changes in scope and funding.
Requirements: U.S. bachelor's degree in applied linguistics/cross-cultural studies is preferred; U.S. master's degree in applied linguistics/American studies is preferred. One year's teaching experience is required. Previous international experience is preferred.
Duration: One year; renewable for one year.
Benefits: Salary and benefits were unknown at time of publication.
Application: January.
Contact: Julio Parada, Director, Departmento Artes y Letras, Universided de La Serena, Casilla 599, La Serena, Chile.

COLOMBIA

Colegio Bolivar,
Apdo. Aereo 4875, Cali, Colombia.
    This private, coed primary/secondary institution was founded in 1948. Academic calendar runs from August to June. Primary language of instruction is English; secondary language of instruction is Spanish. Current enrollment is 800; 50 percent of faculty are U.S. nationals.
Opportunities: Ten to 15 positions for teachers of self-contained classes, grades one through six, and for teachers of mathematics, English, physics, social studies, music, and physical education, grades seven through 12. Two to three positions available for teachers of English as a second language.
Requirements: U.S. bachelor's degree in appropriate field is required; U.S. master's degree is preferred. Spanish language proficiency on the intermediate level is preferred.

Three years' teaching experience is preferred. Student teaching during university training is required.

For *TESL/TEFL:* U.S. bachelor's degree in applied linguistics is required; U.S. master's degree in applied linguistics is preferred. Spanish language proficiency on the advanced level is required. Three years' teaching experience is required. Previous international experience is preferred.

Duration: Two years; renewable.

Benefits: Salary is $11,000–$15,000 per year for teachers; $26,000–$36,000 per year for administrators. Two-day pre-assignment orientation in Miami. Transportation is included for appointee and dependents. Housing is not included; approximate cost of housing is $150–$250 per month. Free tuition for two children is available. Shared premiums for Blue Cross/Blue Shield, local health insurance, and Colombian retirement plan. Freight allowance of 150 lbs. per person.

Application: February; notification no later than June. Personal interview is required; school representative tours United States annually in February/March.

Contact: Dr. Curtis C. Harvey, Director, Colegio Bolivar, Apdo. Aereo 4875, Cali, Colombia.

Colegio Karl C. Parrish,
Apdo. Aereo 950, Barranguilla, Colombia.

This private, coed primary/secondary institution was founded in 1938. Academic calendar runs from mid-August to mid-June. Primary language of instruction is English; secondary language of instruction is Spanish. Current enrollment is 800; 50 percent of faculty are U.S. nationals.

Opportunities: About 12 positions annually for teachers of self-contained classes, grades pre-kindergarten through eight, and for teachers of English, mathematics, biology, chemistry, physics, and social studies on the secondary level. Also openings for teachers of accounting and computers on the vocational-secondary level.

Requirements: U.S. bachelor's degree in appropriate field is required; U.S. master's degree is preferred. Two years' teaching experience is required. Previous international experience is preferred.

Duration: One year; renewable.

Benefits: Salary is $17,000–$20,000 per year. Two-day pre-assignment orientation in Miami. Transportation is included for appointee only. Housing is not included; approximate cost of housing is $400–$500 per month. Free tuition for one child is available. Blue Cross/Major Medical is provided.

Application: February; notification by late March.

Contact: Director, Colegio Karl C. Parrish, Apdo. Aereo 950, Barranguilla, Colombia.

Colegio Nueva Granada,
Apdo. Aereo 51339, Bogota, Colombia.

This private, coed primary/secondary institution, with facilities for special education of the learning disabled, was founded in 1938. Academic calendar runs from September to June. Primary language of instruction is English; secondary language of instruction is Spanish. Current enrollment is 1,350; 70 percent of faculty are non-native; 68 percent of faculty are U.S. nationals.

Opportunities: About 15 positions annually for teachers of all subjects on the primary level; for teachers of physics, chemistry, and mathematics on the secondary level; and specialists in education of the learning disabled.

Requirements: U.S. bachelor's degree in appropriate field is required. Two years' teaching experience is preferred.

Duration: Two years; renewable.

Benefits: Salary is $11,000–$18,000. Three-week pre-assignment orientation in Bogota. Transportation is included for appointee and spouse if both are teachers. Housing is not included; approximate cost of housing is $400 per month. Home leave is included after two years. Free tuition for dependent children is available. Percentage of Blue Cross/Blue Shield is paid.

Application: March 1; notification by April 15.

Contact: Les Landers, Colegio Nueva Granada, Apdo. Aereo 51339, Bogota, Colombia.

Columbus School,
Calle 78B #73-108, Medellín, Colombia.

This private, coed primary/secondary institution was founded in 1945. Academic calendar runs from August to June. Primary language of instruction is English; other language of instruction is Spanish. Current enrollment is 970; 67 percent of faculty are U.S. nationals.

Opportunities: About 15 positions annually for kindergarten teachers and teachers of general and physical education on the primary level, and mathematics, biology, English, social studies, and physical education teachers on the secondary level. Counselors and teachers of English as a second language are also needed.

Requirements: U.S. bachelor's degree in education or appropriate field is required; U.S. master's degree is preferred. Spanish language proficiency is preferred. Two years' teaching experience is preferred. Valid teaching certificate is required.

For *TESL/TEFL:* U.S. bachelor's or master's degree in applied linguistics or English is preferred. Spanish language proficiency on the advanced level is preferred. Two years' teaching experience is required. Previous international experience is preferred.

Duration: Two years; renewable.

Benefits: Salary is $10,000–$15,000. Two-day pre-assignment orientation in Miami. Transportation is included for appointee only. Housing is included. Maximum three scholarships are granted. Overseas Blue Cross/Blue Shield is provided.

Application: February 1; notification by May.

Contact: Superintendent, Columbus School, Apdo. Aereo 5225, Medellín, Colombia.

George Washington School,
Apdo. Aereo 2899, Cartagena, Colombia.

This private, coed primary/secondary institution was founded in 1952. Academic calendar runs from August to June. Primary language of instruction is English; secondary language of instruction is Spanish. Current enrollment is 435; 80 percent of faculty are U.S. nationals.

Opportunities: About five to eight positions annually for teachers of self-contained classes on the primary level, and English, science, and mathematics teachers on the secondary level.

Requirements: U.S. bachelor's degree in education is required. Spanish language proficiency on the beginning level is preferred. Five years' teaching experience is preferred. Previous international experience is preferred.

Duration: Two years; renewable.

Benefits: Salary varies; with bachelor's degree and no experience, starting salary is $10,500. Three-day pre-assignment orientation in Miami. Transportation is included. Housing is not included. Free tuition for dependent children is available. Medical insurance is provided. Annual bonus is included.

Application: February 28; notification by mid-April.

Contact: Roger Krakusin, Director, George Washington School, Apdo. Aereo 2899, Cartegena, Colombia.

COSTA RICA

Embassy of Costa Rica,
2112 S St. NW, Washington, DC 20008.

Academic calendar runs from March to December. Primary language of instruction is Spanish; secondary language of instruction is English; other language of instruction is French.

The Embassy reports that there is no need for U.S. teachers, educational administrators, or teachers of English as a second/foreign language at the present time.

Lincoln School,
P.O. Box 1919, San Jose, Costa Rica.

This is a private, coed special-education institution focusing on learning disabilities. Academic calendar runs from March to November. Primary language of instruction is English; secondary language of instruction is Spanish; other language of instruction is

French. Current enrollment is 1,400; 25 percent of faculty are non-native; 24 percent of faculty are U.S. nationals.
Requirements: U.S. bachelor's degree in education is required; U.S. master's degree in education is preferred. One year's teaching experience is preferred.
For *TESL/TEFL:* U.S. bachelor's degree in applied linguistics is preferred. One year's teaching experience is preferred.
Duration: One year; renewable.
Benefits: Salary is $5,000 per year. Transportation is included for appointee only. Housing is included.
Application: October; notification by November.
Contact: Keith D. Miller, Lincoln School, P.O. Box 1919, San Jose, Costa Rica.

DOMINICA

Ministry of Education,
Government Headquarters, Roseau, Commonwealth of Dominica, West Indies.
Academic calendar runs from September to July. Primary language of instruction is English; other languages of instruction are French and Creole.
The Ministry reports that there is no need for U.S. teachers, educational administrators, or teachers of English as a second/foreign language at the present time.

DOMINICAN REPUBLIC

Carol Morgan School of Santo Domingo,
APO Miami 34041.
This private, coed primary/secondary institution was founded in 1933. Academic calendar runs from September to June. Primary language of instruction is English. Current enrollment is 1,400; 85 percent of faculty are U.S. nationals.
Opportunities: Positions for teachers of kindergarten through grade three and mathematics, science, and English teachers on the secondary level. Teachers of English as a second language may also be needed.
Requirements: U.S. bachelor's degree in appropriate field is required; U.S. master's degree is preferred. Spanish language proficiency on the beginning level is preferred. Two years' teaching experience is preferred. Previous international experience is preferred.
For *TESL/TEFL:* U.S. bachelor's or master's degree in applied linguistics is required. Spanish language proficiency on the beginning level is preferred. Five years' teaching experience is required. Previous international experience is preferred.
Duration: Two years; renewable.
Benefits: Salary is $10,000–$25,000 based upon experience. One-week pre-assignment orientation on campus. Transportation is included for appointee and dependents. Housing allowance is included; approximate cost of housing is $350–$400 per month. Free tuition for dependent children is available. Health and life insurance provided on a shared-cost basis. A $1,300–$2,000 settling-in allowance is included.
Application: February 1; notification by May 1.
Contact: Superintendent, Carol Morgan School of Santo Domingo, APO Miami 34041.

ECUADOR

American School of Guayaquil,
P.O. Box 3304, Guayaquil, Ecuador.
This private, coed primary/secondary institution was found in 1942. Academic calendar runs from May to January. Primary language of instruction is Spanish; secondary language of instruction is English. Current enrollment is 1,300; 10 percent of faculty are U.S. nationals.

Opportunities: Two to five positions for teachers of English as a second language and five to eight positions annually for English and social studies teachers on the primary and secondary levels.

Requirements: U.S. bachelor's degree in English is required; U.S. master's degree is preferred. Previous teaching experience is required.

For *TESL/TEFL*: U.S. bachelor's or master's degree in linguistics, English, or teaching English as a second language is required.

Duration: Nine months; renewable for two years.

Benefits: Salary is $4,000. Two-day pre-assignment orientation. Transportation is included for appointee only. Housing is not included; approximate cost of housing is $200 per month. Free tuition for dependent children is available.

Application: March 30.

Contact: Colegio Americano, Box 3304, Guayaquil, Ecuador.

GUATEMALA

Colegio Maya,
Apdo. Postales 64-C, Guatemala.

This is a private, coed primary/secondary institution. Academic calendar runs from September to June. Primary language of instruction is English; secondary language of instruction is Spanish; other languages of instruction are French and German. Current enrollment is 250; 95 percent of faculty are non-native; 90 percent of faculty are U.S. nationals.

Opportunities: Ten positions annually primarily for primary education teachers; positions also available for teachers of English as a second language.

Requirements: U.S. bachelor's degree in appropriate field is required; U.S. master's degree is preferred. Spanish language proficiency on the intermediate level is preferred. Two years' teaching experience is required. Previous international experience is preferred.

For *TESL/TEFL:* U.S. bachelor's degree in English is preferred; U.S. master's degree in teaching English as a second/foreign language is required. Spanish language proficiency is preferred. Two years' teaching experience is required. Previous international experience is preferred.

Duration: One to three years; renewable annually.

Benefits: Salary is $8,000–$10,000 per year. One-week pre-assignment orientation at school. Transportation is included for appointee only. Housing is not included; approximate cost of housing is $250–$500 per month. Tuition discounts for dependent children are available. Medical insurance is provided.

Application: February 1; notification by May 1.

Contact: Director, Colegio Maya, Apdo. Postales 64-C, Guatemala.

HAITI

Haitian-American Institute,
Angle Rue Capois et rue St. Cyr, Port-au-Prince, Haiti.

This public, coed, adult-education binational institution was founded in 1942 to reinforce cultural ties between the U.S. and Haiti. Academic calendar runs from September to September. Primary language of instruction is English; other languages of instruction are Haitian-Creole and French. Current enrollment is 1,000; 50 percent of faculty are U.S. nationals.

Opportunities: Positions annually for teachers of English as a foreign language.

Requirements: U.S. bachelor's degree in liberal arts is required, U.S. bachelor's degree in English is preferred; U.S. master's degree in teaching English as a foreign language is preferred. French language proficiency on the beginning level is preferred. Five years' teaching experience is preferred. Previous international experience is preferred. Must present demonstrated work record.

Duration: No contract.

Benefits: Salary is $4.00–$6.50 per hour. Two-month pre-assignment orientation in Port-au-Prince. Transportation is not included. Housing is not included; approximate cost of housing is $300 per month.
Application: No deadline.
Contact: Director, Academic Dept., Haitian-American Institute, Angle Rue Capois et rue St. Cyr, Port-au-Prince, Haiti.

Union School,
P.O. Box 1175, Port-au-Prince, Haiti.
   This private, coed primary/secondary institution was founded in 1919. Academic calendar runs from late August to late May. Primary language of instruction is English; secondary language of instruction is French; other language of instruction is Spanish. Current enrollment is 350; 74 percent of faculty are U.S. nationals.
   There is no formal employment program for hiring U.S. educators. Listed is general information on faculty recruitment.
Opportunities: Four to six positions available.
Duration: Two years; renewable indefinitely.
Benefits: Salary is based upon a scale. Starting salary with bachelor's degree and no experience is $9,000 per year. Three-day pre-assignment orientation at school. Transportation is included from New York or Miami only. Housing is not included; approximate cost of housing is $300 per month. Tuition reduction is 50 percent for first year, 75 percent for second year, 100 percent thereafter. Major medical and life insurance are provided. Relocation allowance of $500 is included upon first arrival only.
Application: Not given; notification by early April.
Contact: Dr. Marie Bogat, Superintendent, Union School, P.O. Box 1175, Port-au-Prince, Haiti.

HONDURAS

American School,
U.S. Embassy, Tegucigalpa, Honduras.
   This private, coed primary/secondary institution was founded in 1946. Academic calendar runs from August to June. Primary language of instruction is English; secondary language of instruction is Spanish. Current enrollment is 996; 61 percent of faculty are non-native; 52 percent of faculty are U.S. nationals.
Opportunities: Ten to 15 positions annually for teachers on primary and secondary levels. Periodically there is a need for educational administrators.
Requirements: U.S. bachelor's degree in appropriate field is required; U.S. master's degree is preferred. One year's teaching experience is preferred. Previous international experience is preferred.
Duration: Two years; renewable.
Benefits: Three-day pre-assignment orientation in Miami. Transportation is included for appointee only. Housing is not included; approximate cost of housing is $400–$600 per month. Fifty percent tuition reduction is avaiable. Home leave is provided after two years. Blue Cross/Blue Shield is provided. Settling-in allowance of $800 is offered. Annual bonus equal to one month's salary is included.
Application: No deadline.
Contact: Superintendent, American School, c/o U.S. Embassy, Tegucigalpa, Honduras.

International School,
A.P. 565, San Pedro Sula, Honduras.
   This private, coed primary/secondary institution, also offering adult education courses, was founded in 1953. Academic calendar runs from August to June. Primary language of instruction is English; secondary language of instruction is Spanish. Current enrollment is 975; 60 percent of faculty are U.S. nationals.
Opportunities: Ten positions for teachers of self-contained classes on the primary level and teachers of mathematics and science on the secondary level.

Requirements: U.S. bachelor's degree is required; U.S. master's or Ph.D. degree is preferred. Spanish language proficiency on the beginning level is preferred. Two years' teaching experience is preferred. Previous international experience is preferred.
Duration: Three years; renewable for two years.
Benefits: Salary is U.S. $8,000–$11,000 paid in Lempiras. Three-day pre-assignment orientation in Miami. Transportation is included for appointee and dependents. Housing is not included; approximate cost of housing is $200 per month. Scholarships are available for dependent children. Blue Cross/Blue Shield is provided. Home leave is included.
Application: May 1; notification by July.
Contact: Rector, International School, A.P. 565, San Pedro Sula, Honduras. (Send all inquiries airmail.)

JAMAICA

Embassy of Jamaica,
1850 K St. NW, Washington, DC 20006.

Ministry of Education,
2 National Heroes Circle. P.O. Box 498, Kingston, Jamaica.
Academic calendar runs from September to July. Primary language of instruction is English.
The Embassy and Ministry report that there is no need for U.S. teachers, educational administrators, or teachers of English as a second/foreign language at the present time.

U.S. Information Service,
Mutual Life Centre, 2 Oxford Rd., Kingston 5, Jamaica, W.I.
The USIS Office primarily acts as a counseling service to students wishing to study in the United States.
Opportunities: *Fulbright Lecture Program.* One position annually for a university-level lecturer in mass communications and economics.
Requirements: U.S. Ph.D. degree in communications research or economics is preferred. Five years' teaching experience is required. Previous international experience is preferred.
Duration: One academic year; renewable for one academic year.
Benefits: Salary varies. Transportation is included for appointee and dependents. University housing is included.
Application: October.
Contact: U.S. Information Agency, 400 C St. SW, Washington, DC 20547.

Priory School,
32 Hope Rd., Kingston 10, Jamaica.
This private, coed primary/secondary institution, with special education/learning disability facilities, was founded in 1944. Academic calendar runs from September to June. Primary language of instruction is English; other languages of instruction are French and Spanish. Current enrollment is 575; 43 percent of faculty are non-native; 21 percent of faculty are U.S. nationals.
Opportunities: Positions for guidance counselor and teacher of English as a second language on the primary level; teachers of mathematics, U.S. history/government, English as a second language, English, physical education, and student activities director on the secondary level; and specialists to work with learning-disabled students.
Requirements: U.S. bachelor's degree in education is required; U.S. master's or Ph.D. degree in appropriate field is preferred. One to three years' teaching experience is preferred; student teaching is accepted. Previous international experience is preferred.
For *TESL/TEFL:* U.S. bachelor's degree in linguistics or education is required; U.S. master's degree is preferred. One to three years' teaching experience is preferred; student teaching is accepted. Previous international experience is preferred.
Duration: Two years; renewable for two years.
Benefits: Salary is on graduated scale based upon experience. Four-day pre-assignment orientation at school. Transportation is included for appointee only. Housing allowance

is included; approximate cost of housing is Jamaican $500 per month. Fifty percent tuition allowance for dependent children is available. Blue Cross, life insurance, and pension plan are provided. Relocation allowance is included.

Application: May; notification three or four months prior to employment.

Contact: Mrs. Georgia Edwards, Priory School, 32 Hope Rd., Kingston 10, Jamaica.

MEXICO

American School Foundation A.C.,
Calle Sur 136 #135 Col. Las Americas Del. A. Obregón, Mexico 01120, D.F.

This private, coed primary/secondary institution, also offering adult-education courses, was founded in 1888. A small facility offering special education was opened in September 1983 admitting six students. Academic calendar runs from September to June. Primary languages of instruction are English and Spanish; other languages of instruction are French and German. Current enrollment is 2,104; 60 percent of faculty are U.S. nationals.

Opportunities: About 20 positions annually for elementary education teachers; mathematics, science, social studies, and physical education teachers on the secondary level; English, accounting, and gymnastics teachers on the adult-education level; and special education teachers. About ten positions available for teachers of English as a second language. In addition, the school reports a need for admissions administrators, counselors, and a school superintendent.

Requirements: U.S. bachelor's degree is required for teachers; U.S. master's degree is required for administrators and counselors; U.S. Ph.D. degree is required for superintendent. Two years' teaching experience is preferred; student teaching counts as experience.

For *TESL/TEFL:* U.S. bachelor's degree in linguistics or English as a second language is required. Two years' teaching experience is preferred; student teaching counts as experience.

Duration: One year; renewable.

Benefits: Salary is 90,000 pesos per month. One-week pre-assignment orientation at school. Transportation is included for appointee only. Housing is not included; approximate cost of housing is 40,000 pesos per month. Tuition discount for dependent children is available. Medical and partial life insurance are provided. Other stipends include food coupons (12% salary), savings plan (13% salary), and social provisions package (30% salary).

Application: Open; most hiring done in May.

Contact: Personnel Officer, American School Foundation A.C., Calle Sur 136 135 Col. Las Americas Del. A. Obregón, Mexico 01120, D.F.

American School Foundation of Guadalajara A.C.,
Colomus 200, Guadalajara, Mexico.

This private, coed primary/secondary institution, also offering adult-education courses, was founded in 1956. Academic calendar runs from September to June. Primary language of instruction is English; secondary language of instruction is Spanish; other language of instruction is French. Current enrollment is 1,150; 40 percent of faculty are U.S. nationals.

There is no formal employment program for hiring U.S. educators. Listed is general information on faculty recruitment.

Opportunities: About 20 positions available, 50 percent on primary level and 25 percent on secondary level.

Requirements: U.S. bachelor's degree and teacher certification is required. Two years' teaching experience is preferred. Previous international experience is preferred.

For *TESL/TEFL:* U.S. bachelor's degree in English is preferred. Foreign language proficiency on the intermediate level is preferred. Two years' teaching experience is preferred.

Contact: Director, American School Foundation of Guadalajara A.C., Colomus 200, Guadalajara, Mexico.

American School of Pachuca,
Apdo. Postal 131, Pachuca, Hidalgo 42000, Mexico.
This private, coed primary/secondary institution was founded in 1920. Academic calendar runs from September to June. Primary languages of instruction are Spanish and English. Current enrollment is 530; 25 percent of faculty are U.S. nationals.
Opportunities: Ten positions for teachers of all subjects on the primary level, and ten positions for teachers of English as a foreign language on the secondary level.
Requirements: U.S. bachelor's degree in elementary education is required. Two years' teaching experience is preferred.
For *TESL/TEFL:* U.S. bachelor's degree is preferred. Two years' teaching experience is preferred.
Duration: Two years; renewable.
Benefits: Salary information was not provided. Pre-assignment orientation on-site. Transportation is included for appointee only. Housing is included. Educational allowances for dependent children and medical care are provided.
Application: February; notification by June.
Contact: Gerald Selitzer, Director, American School of Pachuca, Apdo. Postal 131, Pachuca, Hidalgo 42000, Mexico.

Colegio Americano de Durango, A.C.
Francisco Sarabia 416 Pte., Apdo. Postal 15-B, Durango, Dgo. 34000, Mexico.
This private, coed primary/secondary institution, also offering English and secretarial classes in afternoons and evenings, was founded in 1954. Academic calendar runs from September to June. Primary language of instruction is English; secondary language of instruction is Spanish. Current enrollment is 640; 67 percent of faculty are Mexican; 33 percent of faculty are U.S. nationals.
Opportunities: About 10 positions annually for teachers of elementary and secondary education, including English as a second language.
Requirements: U.S. master's degree in elementary education is preferred.
Duration: One year; renewable for one year.
Benefits: Salary is $300 per month. One-week pre-assignment orientation. Transportation is included for appointee only. Housing is not included; approximate cost of room and board is $80 per month. Government social security program covers all medical and hospitalization needs.
Application: June 1.
Contact: Kenneth Darg, Director, Colegio Americano de Druango, A.C., Francisco Sarabia 416 Pte., Apdo. Postal, 15-B, Durango, Dgo. 34000, Mexico.

Universidad de las Américas, A.C.
Apdo. Postal 100, Santa Catarina Mártir, 72820 Puebla, Mexico.
This private university was founded in 1940. Academic calendar runs from mid-August to late May. Primary language of instruction is Spanish; secondary language of instruction is English. Current enrollment is 4,000; 30 percent of faculty are non-native; 22.5 percent of faculty are U.S. nationals.
Opportunities: Positions for teachers of engineering, business, liberal and fine arts. Numbers of positions vary according to need.
Requirements: U.S. master's degree in appropriate field is required; U.S. Ph.D. degree is preferred. Spanish language proficiency on the advanced level is preferred. Three years' teaching experience is required. Previous international experience is preferred.
For *TESL/TEFL:* U.S. master's degree in teaching English as a second/foreign language is required. Spanish language proficiency on the intermediate level is required. Three years' teaching experience is required. Previous international experience is preferred.
Duration: Not fixed.
Benefits: Salary varies according to rank experience, and discipline. Transportation is not included. Housing is not included. Free tuition at university is available. University group insurance plan and government social security program are included. Retirement and tax-free savings plans are provided.
Application: March for fall semester.
Contact: Vice-Rector Académico, Universidad de las Américas, A.C., Apdo. Postal 100, Santa Catarina Mártir, 72820 Puebla, Mexico.

Universidad Internacional de Mexico, A.C.,
La Otra Banda 40, Col. Tizapán A. Obregón, 01090 Mexico, D.F.

Universidad Internacional de Mexico is part of a system of U.S. universities based in California. The main campus of the system is United States International University, San Diego.

USIU and its branch campuses specialize in quality U.S. education with an international approach. In Mexico, business and psychology majors, master's degrees, and a broad range of lower-division liberal arts courses are offered. A program for teachers of English as a second language is planned for 1984.

Opportunities: The university is interested in hiring U.S. professors on a continual basis who would complement its staff and bring in outside ideas and technology. Of particular interest would be interinstitutional contacts which would enrich the possibilities offered , and might provide a flow of U.S. students into the international campus environment.

Requirements: U.S. master's degree is required; U.S. Ph.D. degree is preferred. Spanish language proficiency on the advanced level is preferred. Previous teaching experience is preferred. Previous internatinal experience is preferred.

For *TESL/TEFL:* U.S. bachelor's degree is required; U.S. master's or Ph.D. degree is preferred. Spanish language proficiency on the advanced level is preferred. Previous teaching experience is preferred. Previous international experience is preferred.

Benefits: Salary is negotiable; about $1,000 per course. Pre-assignment orientation. Transportation is not included. Housing is not included; approximate cost of housing is $500 per month.

Application: Varies; about six months prior to starting date.

Contact: T. Noel Osborn, Universidad Internacional de Mexico, A.C., La Otra Banda 40, Col. Tizapán A. Obregón, 01090 Mexico, D.F.

NICARAGUA

American-Nicaraguan School,
P.O. Box 2670, Managua, Nicaragua.

This private, coed primary/secondary institution was founded in 1944. Academic calendar runs from March to December and August to July, with no classes in January and February. Primary language of instruction is English; secondary language of instruction is Spanish. Current enrollment is 635; 50 percent of faculty are U.S. nationals.

Opportunities: About eight positions for teachers of English as a second language on the primary level, teachers of English as a second language, social studies, mathematics, and science on the secondary level. English-as-a-second-language courses are also offered as part of extension/adult education.

Requirements: U.S. bachelor's degree in education is required; U.S. master's degree is preferred. Spanish language proficiency on the intermediate level is preferred. One to five years' teaching experience is preferred. Previous international experience is sometimes preferred, depending on the position.

For *TESL/TEFL:* U.S. bachelor's degree in English as a second language is required; U.S. master's degree in English as second language is preferred. Spanish language proficiency on the intermediate level is preferred. One to five years' teaching experience is preferred. Previous international experience is preferred.

Duration: One year; renewable annually.

Benefits: Salary is $8,000 per year, payable in U.S. dollars (50%) and C'ordobas (50%). One-week pre-assignment orientation on-site. Transportation is included for appointee only; excess baggage allowance of $200 is also included. Housing is included. Tuition benefits for dependent children is available. Life and medical insurance are provided. Hardship-post allotment of $1,000 per year is available.

Application: May for August; December for March.

Contact: Director, American-Nicaraguan School, P.O. Box 2670, Managua, Nicaragua.

PANAMA

Embassy of Panama,
2862 McGill Terrace NW, Washington, DC.
Academic calendar runs from April to December. Primary language of instruction is Spanish; secondary languages of instruction are English and French.
The Embassy reports that there is no need for U.S. teachers, educational administrators, or teachers of English as a second/foreign language at the present time.

PERU

Ministerio de Educacion Nacionales,
Parqué Universitario s/n, Lima, 1-Peru.
Academic calendar runs from April to December. Primary language of instruction is Castellano; secondary language of instruction is English.
The Ministry reports that there is no need for U.S. teachers, educational administrators, or teachers of English as a second/foreign language at the present time. Opportunities are available through the Fulbright-Hays Program.

Commission for Educational Exchange between the United States and Peru,
Maximo Abril 599, Jesus Maria, Lima, Peru.
Opportunities: *Fulbright-Hays Program.* Two to three positions annually for educational administration, educational psychology, and curriculum development on the university level.
Requirements: U.S. bachelor's degree is required; U.S. master's or Ph.D. degree is preferred. Spanish language proficiency on the intermediate or advanced level is preferred. Previous teaching experience is preferred.
Duration: Five months; renewable for three months.
Benefits: Salary is $1,500. Three-day pre-assignment orientation in Lima. Transportation is included on U.S. carrier for appointee only. Housing is not included; approximate cost of housing is $250–$600. Health and accident insurance are provided. Academic expenses allowance and allowance to defray ongoing U.S. expenses are included.
Application: June 30; notification three months prior to assignment.
Contact: Council for International Exchange of Scholars, 11 Dupont Circle, Washington, DC 20036.

American School of Lima (Instituto Educacional Franklin D. Roosevelt),
Apdo. 247, Miraflores, Lima 18, Peru.
This private, coed primary/secondary institution, also offering adult education courses, was founded in 1946. Academic calendar runs from August to June. Primary language of instruction is English; secondary language of instruction is Spanish. Current enrollment is 1,315; 49 percent of faculty are U.S. nationals.
There is no formal employment program for hiring U.S. educators. Listed is general information on faculty recruitment.
Requirements: U.S. bachelor's degree in education and teaching certification are required. Two years' teaching experience is required. Previous international experience is preferred. Teaching couples are preferred.
Duration: Two years; renewable for one or two years.
Benefits: Salary is $9,530–$19,569. Transportation is included. Housing is included. Benefits include free tuition for dependent children, health insurance, school bus transportation, baggage allowance, relocation allowance, and home leave after initial contract completion. The school pays for municipal taxes and water; electricity and telephone bills are the responsibility of teacher.
Application: April.
Contact: Dale I. Swall, Superintendent, American School of Lima (Instituto Educacional Franklin D. Roosevelt), Apdo. 247, Miraflores, Lima 18, Peru.

Prescott Anglo-American School,
Apdo. 1036, Arequipa, Peru.

This private, coed primary/secondary institution, also offering intensive instruction in English as a foreign language was founded in 1965. Academic calendar runs from March to December. Primary language of instruction is Spanish. Current enrollment is 1,150; 17 percent of faculty are non-native; nine percent of faculty are U.S. nationals.

Opportunities: About 10 positions annually, primarily for teachers of English as a foreign language, although teachers are also needed for computer instruction.

Requirements: U.S. bachelor's degree in applied linguistics, English, or teaching English as a second language is preferred. Spanish language proficiency on the beginning level is preferred. Two years' teaching experience is required. Previous international experience is preferred.

Duration: Two years; renewable annually.

Benefits: Salary is 500,000 soles per month (about $300). One-month pre-assignment orientation at school. Transportation is not included. Housing is included. Tuition benefits for dependent children are available. Health insurance covers 80 percent of medical care for appointee and dependents.

Application: June 1. Letters of reference are required.

Contact: Ellen Hazelhurst de Ojeda, Director of Studies, Prescott Anglo-American School, Apdo. 1036, Arequipa, Peru.

SAINT LUCIA, BRITISH WEST INDIES

Ministry of Education and Culture,
Cr. of Laborie and Micoud Sts., Castries, St. Lucia.

Academic calendar runs from September to July. Primary language of instruction is English.

The Ministry reports that there is no need for U.S. teachers or educational administrators at the present time.

TRINIDAD AND TOBAGO

Ministry of Education,
Alexandria St., Port of Spain, Trinidad.

Academic calendar runs from September to August. Primary language of instruction is English. Other languages of instruction are Spanish and French.

The Ministry reports that there is no need for U.S. teachers, educational administrators or teachers of English as a second/foreign language at the present time.

U.S. VIRGIN ISLANDS, SAINT THOMAS

Antilles School,
P.O. Box 7280, St. Thomas, Virgin Islands 00801.

This private, coed primary/secondary institution was founded in 1950. Academic calendar runs from September to mid-June. Primary language of instruction is English. Current enrollment is 355; 90 percent of faculty are non-native; 85 percent of faculty are U.S. nationals.

Opportunities: About three to six positions annually for teachers of self-contained classes (grades prekindergarten through five), U.S. college-preparatory curriculum (grades six through 12), and reading specialists for students with minor learning disabilities.

Requirements: U.S. bachelor's degree in appropriate field is required; U.S. master's or Ph.D. degree is preferred. Three years' teaching experience is preferred.

Duration: One year; renewable. Average duration is six years.
Benefits: Salary is $11,000–$14,000. Transportation is not included. Housing is not included; approximate cost of housing is $250–$1,000 per month. Full medical insurance, life insurance at 150 percent of salary and TIAA/CREF are provided.
Application: February to April.
Contact: Headmaster, Antilles School, P.O. Box 7280, St. Thomas, Virgin Islands 00801.

VENEZUELA

Colegio Internacional de Carabobo,
Apdo. 103, Valencia, Venezuela.
  This is a private, coed primary/secondary institution. Academic calendar runs from August to June. Primary language of instruction is English; secondary language of instruction is Spanish. Current enrollment is 300; 83 percent of faculty are U.S. nationals.
Opportunities: Six to ten positions annually. Single teachers only; no dependents accepted.
Requirements: U.S. bachelor's degree in appropriate field is required; U.S. master's degree is preferred. Spanish language proficiency on the beginning level is preferred. Three years' teaching experience is required.
Duration: One year; renewable.
Benefits: Salary is $15,000–$22,000. One-week pre-assignment orientation on-site. Transportation is included for appointee only. Housing is included. Basic health insurance is provided.
Application: January.
Contact: Frank Anderson, Colegio Internacional de Carabobo, Apdo. 103, Valencia, Venezuela.

Escuela Anaco,
Apdo. 31, Anaco, Venezuela.
  This private, coed primary-level institution was founded in 1956. Academic calendar runs from late August to May. Primary language of instruction is English; secondary language of instruction is Spanish. Current enrollment is 44; 86 percent of faculty are U.S. nationals.
  There is no formal employment program for hiring U.S. educators. Listed is general information on faculty recruitment.
Requirements: U.S. bachelor's degree in education and teaching certification is required; U.S. master's degree in education is preferred. Three years' teaching experience is required.
Duration: One year; renewable for one year.
Benefits: Salary is based upon background and experience. Transportation is included for appointee only. Housing is included. Medical insurance is included. Personal automobile is provided.
Application: April 15.
Contact: Director, Escuela Anaco, Apdo. 31, Anaco, Venezuela.

Escuela Campo Alegre S.A.,
Apdo. del Este 60382, Caracas 1060-A, Venezuela.
  This private, coed primary/secondary institution was founded in 1937. Academic calendar runs from August to June. Primary language of instruction is English; secondary language of instruction is Spanish; other language of instruction is French. Current enrollment is 650; 87 percent of faculty are non-native; 75 percent of faculty are U.S. nationals.
  There is no formal employment program for hiring U.S. educators. Listed is general information on faculty recruitment.
Opportunities: About one to four positions annually for teachers of grades prekindergarten through three, four through six, seven through nine, and specialists in working with the learning-disabled.

Requirements: U.S. bachelor's degree in education is required; U.S. master's degree in education is preferred; U.S. Ph.D. degree in education administration is preferred. Two years' teaching experience is required. Previous international experience is preferred.
Duration: Two years; renewable.
Benefits: Salary is based upon qualifications. Three- to four-day pre-assignment orientation on-site. Transportation is usually included for appointee only. Housing is not included; approximate cost of housing is 4,000–8,000 rolivares. Tuition benefits for dependent children are available. Medical insurance is provided. A Christmas bonus is given.
Application: March/April.
Contact: Dr. Roland Roth, Superintendent, Escuela Campo Alegre S.A., Apdo. del Este 60382, Caracas 1060-A, Venezuela.

SOURCES OF ADDITIONAL INFORMATION

Association of University Programs in Health Administration (AUPHA),
Suite 503, 1911 Fort Myer Dr., Arlington, VA 22209.

Founded in 1948, AUPHA maintains both institutional and individual membership serving worldwide teachers, lecturers, guidance counselors, curriculum developers, and researchers. It maintains an extensive network of all programs in the health administration field for member placement.

AUPHA provides fellowships for foreign faculty to teach in the United States and provides contacts for exchanges. It will also contact foreign institutions on behalf of interested U.S. nationals and will counsel on possible funding sources.

AUPHA's publication, *Health Services Administration 1983-85,* a worldwide program guide, is available for $10.

Association for World Education,
P.O. Box 589, Huntington, NY 11743.

The Association for World Education, founded in 1970, maintains individual and institutional membership. Its services include general information and publications, including the *Journal of World Education,* and quarterly newsletters.

The Association describes its function as "promoting and encouraging all types of innovative education programs with a world perspective or problem-solving orientation." The Association does not have a formal program for employing U.S. teachers or educational administrators abroad, although it provides the avenue to interchange ideas and experiences by cosponsoring conferences on peace studies and world education.

Education Information Service (EIS),
15 Orchard St., Wellesley Hills, MA 02181.

Education Information Service periodically publishes a list of openings in the United States for teachers and administrators on the primary, secondary, and undergraduate levels. A similar publication describes positions abroad for U.S. educators. In addition, EIS publishes special studies on locating teaching positions in the People's Republic of China, Japan, Australia, New Zealand, Saudi Arabia, the U.S. Virgin Islands, Alaska, England, France, Italy, Spain, and Switzerland.

The "Instant Alert Service" notifies individual clients of appropriate openings in their fields in the desired geographic area on the same day that EIS learns of the position. This service charges a $29.95 fee for 12 direct, personal notices.

To order any of EIS' publications, write for their publications catalog to EIS, Box 662, Newton, MA 02162.

Modern Language Association (MLA),
62 Fifth Ave., New York, NY 10011.

The Modern Language Association, a U.S.-based association serving teachers, lecturers, and instructors of English as a second/foreign language, was founded in 1883. MLA maintains both individual and institutional membership.

Information concerning U.S. and overseas positions for teachers of English as a second language is included in MLA's quarterly *Job Information Lists* published in October, December, February, and April. Each edition contains information on possible as well as definite openings. Most such positions require a master's degree and several years' experience in the field.

The association also publishes several books, periodicals, and newsletters which can be useful to educators. The MLA publications catalog is available upon request.

Overseas Placement Service for Educators,
152 Gilchrist Hall, University of Northern Iowa, Cedar Falls, IA 50614.

The Overseas Placement Service for Educators of the University of Northern Iowa holds the Midwest Overseas Recruiting Fair annually. Well over 150 educators were hired at each of the last three Fairs, and administrators representing more than 60 overseas schools interviewed 600 highly qualified candidates at the most recent Fair. The 1984 Fair will be held in mid-February.

The Overseas Placement Service for Educators also includes the Vacancy Listing Service, in which registered candidates receive notification of available teaching positions overseas. All candidates must be certified to teach in at least one of the 50 states, and almost all have at least two years of teaching experience.

The fee for candidates wishing to participate in the 1984 Midwest Overseas Recruiting Fair and to receive the Vacancy Listing Service is $40 for individual registrants, $60 for teaching couples. The fee for candidates wishing to receive the Vacancy Listing Service only is $20 for individual registrants, $25 for teaching couples. There is an additional fee of $15 charged to registrants with mailing addresses outside the United States.

Teachers of English to Speakers of Other Languages (TESOL),
202 D.C. Transit Building, Georgetown University, Washington, DC 20057.

TESOL, founded in 1966, serves teachers, lecturers, administrators, guidance counselors, curriculum developers, and researchers involved in English-as-a-second/foreign-language training. TESOL acts as a clearinghouse and includes descriptions of job openings in its bimonthly bulletin sent to member subscribers. A one-year domestic subscription is $3; a one-year overseas subscription is $4.50.

TESOL's membership is worldwide and includes both individual and institutional categories. The annual membership fee ranges from $15 for a student membership to $150 for a commercial membership.

Publications include the *TESOL Quarterly,* a journal devoted to the teachers of English as a second language on all educational levels; the *TESOL Newsletter,* which informs members of state, regional, national, and international professional meetings, in-service opportunities, and other developments related to the profession; the *TESOL Membership Directory; Directory of Teacher Preparation Programs; On TESOL,* which contains selected papers from the annual convention; and occasional special publications such as bibliographies, focus reports, and papers dealing with classroom practices. A complete list of TESOL publications is available upon request.

EMBASSY LISTING

AFGHANISTAN
Embassy of the Democratic Republic of Afghanistan
2341 Wyoming Ave. NW
Washington, DC 20008

ALGERIA
Embassy of the Democratic and Popular Republic of Algeria
2118 Kalorama Rd. NW
Washington, DC 20008

ANTIGUA AND BARBUDA
Embassy of Antigua and Barbuda
2000 N St. NW, Suite 601
Washington, DC 20036

ARGENTINA
Embassy of the Argentine Republic
1600 New Hampshire Ave. NW
Washington, DC 20009

AUSTRALIA
Embassy of Australia
1601 Massachusetts Ave. NW
Washington, DC 20036

AUSTRIA
Embassy of Austria
2343 Massachusetts Ave. NW
Washington, DC 20008

BAHAMAS
Embassy of the Commonwealth of the Bahamas
600 New Hampshire Ave. NW, Suite 865
Washington, DC 20037

BAHRAIN
Embassy of the State of Bahrain
3502 International Dr. NW
Washington, DC 20008

BANGLADESH
Embassy of the People's Republic of Bangladesh
3421 Massachusetts Ave. NW
Washington, DC 20007

BARBADOS
Embassy of Barbados
2144 Wyoming Ave. NW
Washington, DC 20008

BELGIUM
Embassy of Belgium
3330 Garfield St. NW
Washington, DC 20008

BELIZE
Embassy of Belize
1575 I St. NW, Suite 695
Washington, DC 20005

BENIN
Embassy of the People's Republic of Benin
2737 Cathedral Ave. NW
Washington, DC 20008

BOLIVIA
Embassy of Bolivia
3014 Massachusetts Ave. NW
Washington, DC 20008

BOTSWANA
Embassy of the Republic of Botswana
4301 Connecticut Ave. NW, Suite 404
Washington, DC 20008

BRAZIL
Brazilian Embassy
3006 Massachusetts Ave. NW
Washington, DC 20008

BULGARIA
Embassy of the People's Republic of Bulgaria
1621 22nd St. NW
Washington, DC 20008

BURMA
Embassy of the Socialist Republic of the Union of Burma
2300 S St. NW
Washington, DC 20008

BURUNDI
Embassy of the Republic of Burundi
2233 Wisconsin Ave. NW, Suite 212
Washington, DC 20007

CAMEROON
Embassy of the United Republic of Cameroon
2349 Massachusetts Ave. NW
Washington, DC 20008

CANADA
Embassy of Canada
1746 Massachusetts Ave. NW
Washington, DC 20036

CAPE VERDE
Embassy of the Republic of Cape Verde
3415 Massachusetts Ave. NW
Washington, DC 20007

CENTRAL AFRICAN REPUBLIC
Embassy of the Central African Republic
1618 22nd St. NW
Washington, DC 20008

CHAD
Embassy of the Republic of Chad
2002 R St. NW
Washington, DC 20009

CHILE
Embassy of Chile
1732 Massachusetts Ave. NW
Washington, DC 20036

CHINA
Embassy of the People's Republic of China
2300 Connecticut Ave. NW
Washington, DC 20008

COLOMBIA
Embassy of Colombia
2118 Leroy Pl. NW
Washington, DC 20008

CONGO, PEOPLE'S REPUBLIC OF
Embassy of the People's Republic of the Congo
4891 Colorado Ave. NW
Washington, DC 20011

COSTA RICA
Embassy of Costa Rica
2112 S St. NW
Washington, DC 20008

CYPRUS
Embassy of the Republic of Cyprus
2211 R St. NW
Washington, DC 20008

CZECHOSLOVAKIA
Embassy of the Czechoslovak Socialist Republic
3900 Linnean Ave. NW
Washington, DC 20008

DENMARK
Royal Danish Embassy
3200 Whitehaven St. NW
Washington, DC 20008

DJIBOUTI
Embassy of the Republic of Djibouti
c/o the Permanent Mission of the
   Republic of Djibouti to the
   United Nations
866 United Nations Plaza, Suite 4011
New York, NY 10017

DOMINICAN REPUBLIC
Embassy of the Dominican Republic
1715 22 St. NW
Washington, DC 20008

ECUADOR
Embassy of Ecuador
2535 15th St. NW
Washington, DC 20009

EGYPT
Embassy of the Arab Republic of Egypt
2310 Decatur Pl. NW
Washington, DC 20008

EL SALVADOR
Embassy of El Salvador
2308 California St. NW
Washington, DC 20008

EQUATORIAL GUINEA
Embassy of Equatorial Guinea
801 Second Ave., Suite 1403
New York, NY 10017

ETHIOPIA
Embassy of Ethiopia
2134 Kalorama Rd. NW
Washington, DC 20008

FIJI
Embassy of Fiji
1140 19th St. NW, 6th floor
Washington, DC 20036

FINLAND
Embassy of Finland
3216 New Mexico Ave. NW
Washington, DC 20016

FRANCE
Embassy of France
2535 Belmont Rd. NW
Washington, DC 20008

GABON
Embassy of the Gabonese Republic
2034 20th St. NW
Washington, DC 20009

GAMBIA, THE
Embassy of the Gambia
1785 Massachusetts Ave. NW
Washington, DC 20036

GERMAN DEMOCRATIC REPUBLIC
Embassy of the German Democratic Republic
1717 Massachusetts Ave. NW
Washington, DC 20036

GERMANY, FEDERAL REPUBLIC OF
Embassy of the Federal Republic of Germany
4645 Reservoir Rd. NW
Washington, DC 20007

GHANA
Embassy of Ghana
2460 16th St. NW
Washington, DC 20009

GREAT BRITIAN
British Embassy
3100 Massachusetts Ave. NW
Washington, DC 20008

GREECE
Embassy of Greece
2221 Massachusetts Ave. NW
Washington, DC 20008

GRENADA
Embassy of Grenada
1701 New Hampshire Ave. NW
Washington, DC 20009

GUATEMALA
Embassy of Guatemala
2220 R St. NW
Washington, DC 20008

GUINEA
Embassy of the Republic of Guinea
2112 Leroy Pl. NW
Washington, DC 20008

GUINEA-BISSAU
Embassy of the Republic of Guinea-Bissau
c/o the Permanent Mission to the United Nations
  of the Republic of Guinea-Bissau
211 E. 43rd St., Suite 604
New York, NY 10017

GUYANA
Embassy of Guyana
2490 Tracy Pl. NW
Washington, DC 20008

HAITI
Embassy of Haiti
2311 Massachusetts Ave. NW
Washington, DC 20008

HONDURAS
Embassy of Honduras
4301 Connecticut Ave. NW, Suite 100
Washington, DC 20008

HUNGARY
Embassy of the Hungarian People's Republic
3910 Shoemaker St. NW
Washington, DC 20008

ICELAND
Embassy of Iceland
2022 Connecticut Ave. NW
Washington, DC 20008

INDIA
Embassy of India
2107 Massachusetts Ave. NW
Washington, DC 20008

INDONESIA
Embassy of the Republic of Indonesia
2020 Massachusetts Ave. NW
Washington, DC 20036

IRELAND
Embassy of Ireland
2234 Massachusetts Ave. NW
Washington, DC 20008

ISRAEL
Embassy of Israel
3514 International Dr. NW
Washington, DC 20008

ITALY
Embassy of Italy
1601 Fuller St. NW
Washington, DC 20009

IVORY COAST
Embassy of the Republic of Ivory Coast
2424 Massachusetts Ave. NW
Washington, DC 20008

JAMAICA
Embassy of Jamaica
1850 K St. NW, Suite 355
Washington, DC 20006

JAPAN
Embassy of Japan
2520 Massachusetts Ave. NW
Washington, DC 20008

JORDAN
Embassy of the Hashemite Kingdom of Jordan
2319 Wyoming Ave. NW
Washington, DC 20008

KENYA
Embassy of Kenya
2249 R St. NW
Washington, DC 20008

KOREA
Embassy of Korea
2370 Massachusetts Ave. NW
Washington, DC 20008

KUWAIT
Embassy of the State of Kuwait
2940 Tilden St. NW
Washington, DC 20008

LAOS
Embassy of the Lao People's Democratic Republic
2222 S St. NW
Washington, DC 20008

LEBANON
Embassy of Lebanon
2560 28th St. NW
Washington, DC 20008

LESOTHO
Embassy of the Kingdom of Lesotho
Caravel Bldg., Suite 300
1601 Connecticut Ave. NW
Washington, DC 20009

LIBERIA
Embassy of the Republic of Liberia
5201 16th St. NW
Washington, DC 20011

LUXEMBOURG
Embassy of Luxembourg
2200 Massachusetts Ave. NW
Washington, DC 20008

MADAGASCAR
  Embassy of the Democratic Republic of Madagascar
  2374 Massachusetts Ave. NW
  Washington, DC 20008

MALAWI
  Malawi Embassy
  Bristol House
  1400 20th St. NW
  Washington, DC 20036

MALAYSIA
  Embassy of Malaysia
  2401 Massachusetts Ave. NW
  Washington, DC 20008

MALI
  Embassy of the Republic of Mali
  2130 R St. NW
  Washington, DC 20008

MALTA
  Embassy of Malta
  2017 Connecticut Ave. NW
  Washington, DC 20008

MAURITANIA
  Embassy of the Islamic Republic of Mauritania
  2129 Leroy Pl. NW
  Washington, DC 20008

MAURITIUS
  Embassy of Mauritius
  4301 Connecticut Ave. NW, Suite 134
  Washington, DC 20008

MEXICO
  Embassy of Mexico
  2829 16th St. NW
  Washington, DC 20009

MOROCCO
  Embassy of Morocco
  1601 21st St. NW
  Washington, DC 20009

NEPAL
  Royal Nepalese Embassy
  2131 Leroy Pl. NW
  Washington, DC 20008

NETHERLANDS
  Embassy of the Netherlands
  4200 Linnean Ave. NW
  Washington, DC 20008

NEW ZEALAND
  Embassy of New Zealand
  37 Observatory Circle NW
  Washington, DC 20008

NICARAGUA
  Embassy of Nicaragua
  1627 New Hampshire Ave. NW
  Washington, DC 20009

NIGER
Embassy of the Republic of Niger
2204 R. St. NW
Washington, DC 20008

NIGERIA
Embassy of Nigeria
2201 M St. NW
Washington, DC 20037

NORWAY
Royal Norwegian Embassy
2720 34th St. NW
Washington, DC 20008

OMAN
Embassy of the Sultanate of Oman
2342 Massachusetts Ave. NW
Washington, DC 20008

PAKISTAN
Embassy of Pakistan
2315 Massachusetts Ave. NW
Washington, DC 20008

PANAMA
Embassy of Panama
2862 McGill Terrace NW
Washington, DC 20008

PAPUA NEW GUINEA
Embassy of Papua New Guinea
1140 19th St. NW, Suite 503
Washington, DC 20036

PARAGUAY
Embassy of Paraguay
2400 Massachusetts Ave. NW
Washington, DC 20008

PERU
Embassy of Peru
1700 Massachusetts Ave. NW
Washington, DC 20036

PHILIPPINES
Embassy of the Philippines
1617 Massachusetts Ave. NW
Washington, DC 20036

POLAND
Embassy of the Polish People's Republic
2640 16th St. NW
Washington, DC 20009

PORTUGAL
Embassy of Portugal
2125 Kalorama Rd. NW
Washington, DC 20008

QATAR
Embassy of the State of Qatar
600 New Hampshire Ave. NW, Suite 1180
Washington, DC 20037

ROMANIA
Embassy of the Socialist Republic of Romania
1607 23rd St. NW
Washington, DC 20008

RWANDA
Embassy of the Republic of Rwanda
1714 New Hampshire Ave. NW
Washington, DC 20009

SAINT LUCIA
Embassy of Saint Lucia
41 E. 42nd St., Rm. 315
New York, NY 10017

SAUDI ARABIA
Embassy of Saudi Arabia
1520 18th St. NW
Washington, DC 20036

SENEGAL
Embassy of the Republic of Senegal
2112 Wyoming Ave. NW
Washington, DC 20008

SEYCHELLES
Embassy of the Republic of Seychelles
c/o the Permanent Mission of Seychelles
   to the United Nations
820 Second Ave., Suite 203
New York, NY 10017

SIERRA LEONE
Embassy of Sierra Leone
1701 19th St. NW
Washington, DC 20009

SINGAPORE
Embassy of Singapore
1824 R St. NW
Washington, DC 20009

SOMALIA
Embassy of the Somali Democratic Republic
600 New Hampshire Ave. NW, Suite 710
Washington, DC 20037

SOUTH AFRICA
Embassy of South Africa
3051 Massachusetts Ave. NW
Washington, DC 20008

SPAIN
Embassy of Spain
2700 15th St. NW
Washington, DC 20009

SRI LANKA
Embassy of the Democratic Socialist Republic of Sri Lanka
2148 Wyoming Ave. NW
Washington, DC 20008

SUDAN
Embassy of the Democratic Republic of the Sudan
2210 Massachusetts Ave. NW
Washington, DC 20008

SURINAME
Embassy of the Republic of Suriname
2600 Virginia Ave. NW, Suite 711
Washington, DC 20037

SWAZILAND
Embassy of the Kingdom of Swaziland
4301 Connecticut Ave. NW
Washington, DC 20008

SWEDEN
Swedish Embassy
600 New Hampshire Ave. NW, Suite 1200
Washington, DC 20037

SWITZERLAND
Embassy of Switzerland
2900 Cathedral Ave. NW
Washington, DC 20008

SYRIA
Embassy of the Syrian Arab Republic
2215 Wyoming Ave. NW
Washington, DC 20008

TANZANIA
Embassy of the United Republic of Tanzania
2139 R St. NW
Washington, DC 20008

THAILAND
Embassy of Thailand
2300 Kalorama Rd. NW
Washington, DC 20008

TOGO
Embassy of the Republic of Togo
2208 Massachusetts Ave. NW
Washington, DC 20008

TRINIDAD AND TOBAGO
Embassy of Trinidad and Tobago
1708 Massachusetts Ave. NW
Washington, DC 20036

TUNISIA
Embassy of Tunisia
2408 Massachusetts Ave. NW
Washington, DC 20008

TURKEY
Embassy of the Republic of Turkey
1606 23rd St. NW
Washington, DC 20008

UGANDA
Embassy of the Republic of Uganda
5909 16th St. NW
Washington, DC 20011

UNION OF SOVIET SOCIALIST REPUBLICS
Embassy of the Union of Soviet Socialist Republics
1125 16th St. NW
Washington, DC 20036

UNITED ARAB EMIRATES
Embassy of the United Arab Emirates
600 New Hampshire Ave. NW, Suite 740
Washington, DC 20037

UPPER VOLTA
Embassy of the Republic of Upper Volta
2340 Massachusetts Ave. NW
Washington, DC 20008

URUGUAY
Embassy of Uruguay
1918 F St. NW
Washington, DC 20006

VENEZUELA
Embassy of Venezuela
2445 Massachusetts Ave. NW
Washington, DC 20008

WESTERN SAMOA
Embassy of Western Samoa
c/o the Permanent Mission of Samoa
to the United Nations
820 Second Ave.
New York, NY 10017

YEMEN
Embassy of the Yemen Arab Republic
600 New Hampshire Ave. NW, Suite 860
Washington, DC 20037

YUGOSLAVIA
Embassy of the Socialist Federal Republic of Yugoslavia
2410 California St. NW
Washington, DC 20008

ZAIRE
Embassy of the Republic of Zaire
1800 New Hampshire Ave. NW
Washington, DC 20009

ZAMBIA
Embassy of the Republic of Zambia
2419 Massachusetts Ave. NW
Washington, DC 20008

ZIMBABWE
Embassy of Zimbabwe
2852 McGill Terrace NW
Washington, DC 20008

DELEGATION OF THE COMMISSION OF THE EUROPEAN COMMUNITIES
Chancery: 2100 M St. NW, Suite 707
Washington, D.C. 20037

CURRENCY EXCHANGE

NATION	CURRENCY	U.S. EXCHANGE RATE**
Algeria	Dinar	.2032
Argentina	Peso	.0668
Australia	Dollar	.92
Austria	Schilling	.0520
Bahamas	Dollar	1.00
Barbados	Dollar	.4971
Belgium	Franc	.0185
Belize	Belize dollar	.50
Bolivia	Peso	.005
Brazil	Cruzeiro	.00125
Burundi	Franc	.0111
Cameroon	CFA franc	.002506
Canada	Dollar	.8110
Central African Republic	CFA franc	.002506
Chile	Peso	.0119
China (Taiwan)	New Taiwan dollar	.0249
Colombia	Peso	.0136
Costa Rica	Colone	.0236
Cyprus	Pound	1.84
Czechoslovakia	Koruna	.165
Denmark	Krone	.1058
Dominica	East Caribbean Dollar	.37
Dominican Republic	Peso	1.00
Ecuador	Sucre	.0122
Egypt	Pound	1.2160
Ethiopia	Birr	.485
Fiji	Dollar	.97
Finland	Markkaa	.1765
France	Franc	.1253
Gabon	CFA franc	.002506
Germany (Democratic Republic of)	Mark	.3832
Germany (Federal Republic of)	Mark	.3832
Ghana	Cedi	.3638
Greece	Drachma	.0107
Guatemala	Quetzal	1.00
Guinea	Syli	1.1785
Haiti	Gourde	.20
Honduras	Lempira	.50
Hungary	Forint	.0227
Iceland	New Krona	.0358
India	Rupee	.0985
Indonesia	Rupiah	.00101
Ireland	Pound	1.1875
Israel	Shekel	.0123
Italy	Lira	.000629
Ivory Coast	CFA franc	.002506
Jamaica	Dollar	.3401
Japan	Yen	.00428
Kenya	Shilling	.075

South Korea	Won	.00126
Kuwait	Dinar	3.4414
Liberia	Dollar	1.00
Luxembourg	Franc	.0185
Malawi	Kwacha	3.38
Mali	Franc	.00125
Malta	Pound	2.277
Mauritius	Rupee	.0881
Nepal	Rupee	.0704
Netherlands	Guilder	.3410
New Zealand	Dollar	.6630
Nicaragua	Cordoba	.10
Nigeria	Naira	1.34
Norway	Krone	.1358
Oman	Rial Omani	2.89
Pakistan	Rupee	.0751
Panama	Balboa	1.00
Papua New Guinea	Kina	1.1785
Peru	Sol	.000476
Philippines	Peso	.0714
Poland	Zloty	.0105
Portugal	Escudo	.00807
Romania	Leu	.2175
Western Samoa	Tala	.62
Saudi Arabia	Riyal	.2875
Singapore	Dollar	.47
Solomon Islands	Dollar	.8455
South Africa	Rand	.8860
Spain	Peseta	.006655 (as of November 17, 1983)
Sri Lanka	Rupee	.041
Suriname	Guilder	.56
Swaziland	Lilangeni	.90
Sweden	Krona	.1280
Switzerland	Franc	.4717
Syria	Pound	.2558
Thailand	Baht	.0434
Togo	CFA franc	.002506
Trinidad and Tobago	Dollar	.415
Tunisia	Dinar	1.415
Turkey	Lira	.00422
Uganda	Shilling	.0047
U.S.S.R.	Ruble	1.3380
United Kingdom	Pound	1.4980
Upper Volta	CFA franc	.002506
Venezuela	Bolivar	.0772
Yemen (North)	Rial	.2183
Yemen (South)	Dinar	2.89
Zaire	Zaire	.0340
Zambia	Kwacha	.8263
Zimbabwe	Dollar	.9530

**Effective October 31, 1983

BIBLIOGRAPHY

This annotated bibliography describes publications that may assist U.S. nationals seeking teaching opportunities abroad. Many of these publications provide practical information on travel and and work abroad, while others provide specific information on overseas schools and postsecondary institutions.

Many of these publications should be available in major public libraries. If you wish to buy any of these books, write directly to the publisher, not to IIE. For books published by IIE, orders should be sent prepaid to:

> Communications Division
> Box TA
> Institute of International Education
> 809 United Nations Plaza
> New York, NY 10017

IIE PUBLICATIONS

Basic Facts on Foreign Study. New York: Institute of International Education, 1982. Single copies free, $10 per 100.

Designed to guide U.S. students to information on the broad range of practical considerations that accompany studying abroad. Valuable advice is given on the choice of program, definition of terms, and financial considerations. An extensive bibliography lists other sources of information.

Bibliography on Higher Education: A world view. Ruthann Evanoff, comp. New York: Institute of International Education, 1981. Single copies free, $10 per 100.

A bibliography compiled for educators and students interested in the field of international educational exchange.

Fulbright Grants and Other Grants for Graduate Study Abroad. New York: Institute of International Education, 1984. Annual. Free.

Lists IIE-administered financial assistance programs available to graduate students for study abroad.

A Guide to Scholarships, Fellowships, and Grants: A selected bibliography. Kathleen Slowik and Diane D'Angelo, comps. New York: Institute of International Education, 1982. Single copies free, $15 per 100.

An annotated list of sources of financial aid for international study.

Handbook on International Study for U.S. Nationals: Study in the American Republics area. Janet Lowenstein and Mary Louise Taylor, eds. New York: Institute of International Education, 1976. $9.95.

Describes the higher education systems of 29 countries in South and Central America, Mexico, the Caribbean, the Bahamas, and Bermuda.

Higher Education Reform: Implications for foreign students. Barbara B. Burn, ed. New York: Institute of International Education, 1979. $11.95.

Seven essays by European authors addressing the problems in certain Western European countries resulting from the influx of foreign (particularly U.S.) students.

The Learning Traveler. 2 vols. Gail A. Cohen, ed. New York: Institute of International Education, 1983. Annual. $9.95 each.

Vol. 1: *U.S. College-Sponsored Programs Abroad: Academic year.* 13th ed.

Lists by country over 800 semester and academic-year study programs abroad (for undergraduates and graduates) that are sponsored by accredited U.S. colleges and universitites.

Vol. 2: *Vacation Study Abroad.* 34th ed.

Lists by country over 900 summer and early-fall study programs offered in countries around the world sponsored by U.S. and foreign institutions and private organizations for secondary school and college students, teachers, other professionals, and retirees.

GENERAL REFERENCE

Commonwealth Universities Yearbook. A. Christodoulou, T. Craig, eds. 59th ed. London: Association of Commonwealth Universities, 1983. Annual. $155. (Available from the International Publications Service, 114 E. 32nd St., New York, NY 10016.)

Information on teaching staff, courses, facilities, activities, and organizations of 240 institutions in the British Commonwealth.

Directory of African Universities. 2nd ed. Accra North, Ghana: Association of African Universities, 1976. (Available from the Association of African Universities, P.O. Box 5744, Accra North, Ghana.)

Describes courses and faculty at 56 universities in 36 African countries.

Directory of American Firms Operating in Foreign Countries. 10th ed. New York: World Trade Academy Press, 1983. $150. 3 vols. (Available from World Trade Academy Press, 50 E. 42nd St., New York, NY 10017.)

Consists of a series of lists pertaining to American firms with subsidiaries and affiliates operating in foreign countries.

Employment Opportunities in Binational Centers Abroad. (Available from the U.S. Information Agency, Recruitment and Development Staff, 400 C St. NW, Washington, DC 20547.)

Lists openings for English teachers in foreign countries.

A Guide to International Educational Exchange and Community Service for People with Disabilities. Susan Sygall. Eugene, OR: Mobility International USA, 1982-83. (Available from Mobility International USA, P.O. Box 3551, Eugene, OR 97403.)

Describes 18 organizations offering educational exchange and international community service programs. Also discusses implications for participants with disabilities.

Guide to Summer Camps and Summer Schools. Porter Sargent Staff, eds. 22nd ed. Boston: Porter Sargent Publishers, 1981. $15. (Available from Porter Sargent Publishers, Inc., 11 Beacon St., Boston, MA 02108.)

Lists over 1,100 summer camps and schools by type, specialty, and individual features. Descriptions include location and enrollment, director's winter address, fees, length of camping period, and other pertinent information.

How to Find Work Teaching English as a Foreign Language. K.J. Heller. Silver Spring, MD: Breakthrough Communications, 1983.

Lists sources for information about teaching abroad and addresses to contact for additional information.

International Directory for Educational Liaison. 1973. $5.50. (Available from the Overseas Liaison Committee, American Council on Education, 11 Dupont Circle, Washington, DC 20036.)

Describes activities of organizations and institutions concerned with education in developing countries.

International Handbook of Universities. H.M.R. Keyes, D.J. Aitken, Ann C.M. Taylor, eds. 8th ed. New York: Walter De Gruyter, Inc., 1981. $99.50. (Available from Walter De Gruyter, Inc., 200 Saw Mill River Rd., Hawthorne, NY 10532.)

A comprehensive directory of universities and other institutes of higher education presented alphabetically, country by country. Includes information on technical and professional education, as well as teacher training and general education.

International Research and Exchanges Board Program Announcement. New York: International Research and Exchanges Board (IREX), 1983-84. Free. (Available from International Research and Exchanges Board (IREX), 655 Third Ave., New York, NY 10017.)

Describes academic exchange programs, including fellowships and travel grants, administered by IREX with Eastern European countries and the U.S.S.R., for U.S. college or university faculty, eligible scholars, and advanced doctoral candidates who have completed all requirements for the Ph.D. except the thesis.

The ISS Directory of Overseas Schools. Nancy Hayfield, ed. Princeton, NJ: International Schools Services, 1982/83. $15. (Available from International Schools Services, Inc., 126 Alexander St., P.O. Box 5910, Princeton, NJ 08540.)

Up-to-date listing of international schools and educational programs for English-speaking students by country and by city.

Schools Abroad of Interest to Americans. Porter Sargent Staff, eds. 5th ed. Boston: Porter Sargent Publishers, 1982. $22. (Available from Porter Sargent Publishers, Inc., 11 Beacon St., Boston, MA 02108.)

Listing of schools abroad. Provides brief descriptions of size, grade levels, costs, and curriculum. Special section on educational systems of other nations.

U.S. Nonprofit Organizations in Development Assistance Abroad. New York: American Council of Voluntary Agencies for Foreign Service, 1978. $6. (Available from the American Council of Voluntary Agencies for Foreign Service, 200 Park Ave. S., New York, NY 10003.)

Profiles nonprofit organizations. Includes information on agency structure, objectives, programs, and countries of assistance, as well as financial and personnel data.

Work, Study, Travel Abroad: The whole world handbook, 1984-85. Margaret Sherman. 7th ed. New York: St. Martin's Press, 1983. $6.95 plus $2.25 for 1st class postage. (Available from the Council on International Educational Exchange (CIEE), 205 E. 42nd St., New York, NY 10017.)

Provides answers to most frequently asked questions about work, travel, and summer and academic-year study worldwide. Over 800 study and travel programs of U.S. higher-education institutions and national organizations are described.

World List of Universities: 1982-1984. D.J. Aitken, Ann C.M. Taylor, eds. 15th ed. Hawthorne, NY: Walter De Gruyter, Inc., 1982. $59. (Available from Walter De Gruyter, Inc., 200 Saw Mill River Rd., Hawthorne, NY 10532.)

A directory of universities and other institutes of higher education, presented country by country.

The World of Learning. 33rd ed. London: Europa Publications, 1983. $155. 2 vols. (Available from the International Publications Service, 114 E. 42nd St., New York, NY 10016.)

Information on more than 400 international, educational, scientific, and cultural organizations, as well as full descriptions of universities and colleges in 157 countries and territories around the world.

GOVERNMENT PUBLICATIONS

Federal Jobs Overseas. 1979. $.90. (Available from the Superintendent of Documents, U.S. Government Printing Office, Washington, DC 20402.)

Opportunities Abroad for Teachers. Annual. Free. (Available from the International Exchange Branch, Division of International Education, Office of Education, U.S. Dept. of Education, Washington, DC 20202.)

Study and Teaching Opportunities Abroad: Sources of Information About Overseas Study, Teaching, Work, and Travel. 1984. $9. (Available from U.S. Government Printing Office, Washington, DC 20042.)

Lists sources of information and publications about teaching abroad.

Teaching Opportunities—A Directory of Placement Information. $.25. (Available from the U.S. Dept. of Education, Washington, DC 20202.)

Includes material on domestic and foreign teaching opportunities, requirements and salaries for colleges, public, and private schools.

Tips for Travelers to the People's Republic of China. Washington, DC: U.S. Government Printing Office, 1984. $1.75. (Available from U.S. Government Printing Office, Washington, DC 20042.)

Provides information on visas, travel arrangements, customs and currency regulations, and dual citizenships.

TRAVEL

All Asia Guide. Michael Lynch, ed. 11th ed. Rutland, VT: Charles E. Tuttle Co. Inc., 1981. Annual. $7.95. (Available from Charles E. Tuttle Co., Inc., P.O. Box 410, 28 S. Main St., Rutland, VT 05701.)
Travel information for all of Asia..

Budget Travel in Canada. Canadian Universities and Travel Service and Jay Myers, eds. New York: St. Martin's Press, 1982. $10.95. (Available from St. Martin's Press, 175 Fifth Ave., New York, NY 10010.)
A guide to Canada for those traveling on a tight budget. Extensive historical and travel information.

Europe by Eurail. George Ferguson, ed. New York: Burt Franklin and Co., 1983-84. Annual. $8.95. (Available from Lenox Hill Publishing and Distributing Corporation, 235 E. 44th St., New York, NY 10017.)
Itineraries for 21 major cities. Detailed information on using railpasses.

Fisher Annotated Travel Guides. Robert C. Fisher. New York: New American Library, 1983. $11.95 each. (Available from New American Library, 120 Woodbine St., Bergenfield, NJ 07621.)
Each guide contains tourist information on a particular country.

A Handbook for Travellers in India, Pakistan, Nepal, Bangladesh, and Sri Lanka. L.F. Rushbook Williams, ed. 22nd ed. New York: Facts on File, 1982. $35. (Available from Facts on File, 460 Park Ave. S., New York, NY 10016.)
Comprehensive guide to the subcontinent. Contains extensive information on Asian art, religion, history, and architecture. Contains maps.

How to Stay Healthy While Traveling: A guide for today's world traveler. Bob Young, M.D. Santa Barbara, CA: Ross-Erickson, Inc., 1980. $4.95. (Available from P.O. Box 567, Dept. W., Santa Barbara, CA 93102.)
Discusses the essentials of medical care and illness-preventing measures for healthy young travelers.

Let's Go: Britain and Ireland. Harvard Student Agencies. New York: St. Martin's Press, 1983. Annual. $7.95. (Available from St. Martin's Press, 175 Fifth Ave., New York, NY 10010.)
Comprehensive travel guide to Britain and Ireland. Researched and written by students.

Let's Go: Europe. Harvard Student Agencies. New York: St. Martin's Press, 1983. Annual $8.95. (Available from St. Martin's Press, 175 Fifth Ave., New York, NY 10010.)
Guide for traveling in Europe. Information on all aspects of travel. Includes 50 maps. Researched and written by students.

Let's Go: France. Harvard Student Agencies. New York: St. Martin's Press, 1983. Annual. $7.95. (Available from St. Martin's Press, 175 Fifth Ave., New York, NY 10010.)
Comprehensive travel guide to France. Researched and written by students.

Let's Go: Italy. Harvard Student Agencies. New York: St. Martin's Press, 1983. Annual. $7.95. (Available from St. Martin's Press, 175 Fifth Ave., New York, NY 10010.)
Comprehensive guide to travel in Italy. Researched and written by students.

Let's Go: Greece, Israel, and Egypt. Harvard Student Agencies. New York: St. Martin's Press, 1983. Annual. $7.95. (Available from St. Martin's Press, 175 Fifth Ave., New York, NY 10010.)
Comprehensive travel guide to Greece, Israel, and Egypt. Researched and written by students.

The People's Guide to Mexico. Carl Franz. Sante Fe, NM: John Muir Publications, 1983. $10.50. (Available from John Muir Publications, P.O. Box 613, Sante Fe, NM 87501.) A humorous, earthy, and practical guide to travel in Mexico.

The South American Handbook. John Brooks, ed. 59th ed. Chicago: Rand McNally and Co., 1983. Annual. $29.95 (Available from Rand McNally and Co., P.O. Box 7600, Chicago, IL 60680.) Information on facilities and travel throughout South America, Mexico, and the Caribbean. An authoritative guide to all of Latin America.

The Travel Book: Guide to the travel guides. Jon O. Heise and Dennis O'Reilly. New York: R.R. Bowker Co., 1981. $26.95. (Available from R.R. Bowker Co., 1180 Ave. of the Americas, New York, NY 10036.) Reviews 600 English-language travel guide books.

Travel, Study, and Research in Sweden. Adele Heilborn. 7th ed. Stockholm: Sweden-American Foundation, 1975. (Available from Heritage Resource Center, P.O. Box 26305, Minneapolis, MN 55426.) A complete and practical guide to Sweden for persons planning a visit for any length of time. Includes appendix updating the book to June 1979.

Traveler's Survival Kit: Europe. Roger Brown, ed. 4th ed. Cincinnati: Writer's Digest Books, 1982. $7.95. (Available from Writer's Digest Books, 9933 Alliance Rd., Cincinnati, OH 45242.) Provides information on European rules of the road, telephone systems, public transportation, shopping hours, law, and accommodations.

West Asia on a Shoestring. Tony Wheeler. Rev. ed. Sydney: Lonely Planet Publications, 1982. $7.95. (Available from Hippocrene Books, Inc., 171 Madison Ave., New York, NY 10016.) Travel information for Australia, Asia, and the Indian subcontinent.

WORK & STUDY

Alternative Careers for Ph.D's in the Humanities: A selected bibliography. Christine P. Donaldson and Elizabeth A. Flynn. New York: Modern Language Association, 1982. $5.75. (Available from the Modern Language Association, 62 Fifth Ave., New York, NY 10011.) Intended for Ph.D's in the humanities seeking employment outside their discipline. Two sections discuss international and foreign-language careers. A list of useful addresses is appended.

American Education Programs in Austria. Austrian Institute. New York: Austrian Institute, 1982. Free. (Available from the Austrian Institute, 11 E. 52nd St., New York, NY 10022.) Information on academic-year and summer study programs sponsored by U.S. colleges and universities. Updated periodically.

Basic Data on International Courses Offered in the Netherlands 1984-85. The Hague: Netherlands Universities Foundation for International Cooperation (NUFFIC), 1983. Annual. (Available from NUFFIC, 251 Badhuisweg, The Hague LS2509-P.O. Box 90734.) Listing of all international courses offered in the Netherlands.

Careers in Foreign Languages: A handbook. June L. Sherif. Rev. ed. New York: Regents Publishing Co., 1975. $3.95. (Available from Regents Publishing Co., 2 Park Ave., New York, NY 10016.) Discusses foreign languages in relation to occupations. Lists degree requirements for such occupations from primary school to college, proficiency levels required, and scholarships, fellowships and loans offered. Special section on the training of the multilingual. Includes recommendations regarding overseas employment with a general survey of federal government departments' and agencies' occupational opportunities.

The Directory of Jobs and Careers Abroad. Philip Dodd, ed. 5th ed. Oxford: Vacation Work, 1983. (Available from Escape Publications, 5629 Kirkwood Place N., Seattle, WA 98103.)

Although designed for British nationals, this directory does provide useful information and addresses for Americans seeking work in Great Britain.

Directory of Overseas Summer Jobs. David Woodworth. Oxford: Vacation Work, 1983. Annual. $7.95. (Available from Writer's Digest Books, 9933 Alliance Rd., Cincinnati, OH 45242.)

List over 500 jobs worldwide and provides information on visa and work permit regulations.

The Directory of Overseas Summer Jobs in Britain. Susan Griffith, ed. Cincinnati: Writer's Digest Books, 1983. Annual. $7.95. (Available from Writer's Digest Books, 9933 Alliance Rd., Cincinnati, OH 45242.)

Lists 30,000 jobs, including teaching, in Scotland, Wales, England, the Channel Islands, and Northern Ireland. Information on whom to contact, length of employment, number of openings, pay rates, duties, and qualifications. Also includes information on visa and work permit regulations.

Education in Britain. New York: British Information Services, 1982. Updated periodically. (Available from British Information Services, 845 Third Ave., New York, NY 10022.)

Offers complete information on the educational system in Great Britain.

Educational Opportunities in Africa 1974. 2nd ed. Geneva: International University Exchange Fund, 1974. (Available from International University Exchange Fund, P.O. Box 348, 1211 Geneva 11, Switzerland.)

Published in English or French (please specify edition), this directory lists 350 universities, technical colleges, trade schools, teacher-training colleges, and agricultural schools in the independent African countries.

Educator's Passport to International Jobs. Rebecca Anthony and Gerald Roe. Princeton, NJ: Peterson's Guides, 1984. $9.95. (Available from Peterson's Guides Inc., Box 2123, Princeton, NJ 08540.)

Provides positive, straightforward advice regarding every aspect of overseas employment.

Emploi D'Ete. Paris: Vac-Job, 1983. Annual. $7.95. (Available from Council on International Educational Exchange, 205 E. 42nd St., New York, NY 10017.)

A detailed list of summer employment opportunities in France.

Federal Republic of Germany: A directory for teachers and students. New York: German Information Center, 1980. Free. (Available from the German Information Center, 410 Park Ave., New York, NY 10022.)

Directory of organizations and services providing information for Americans interested in studying in Germany.

Finland and its Students. Helsinki: National Union of Finnish Students-SYL, 1982. (Available from the National Union of Finnish Students-SYL, Mannerheiminitie 5 C, 4th floor, 00100 Helsinki 10.)

Provides practical information for U.S. nationals studying in Finland. Includes general information and sections on education and student life.

Higher Education in France: University studies. New York: French Cultural Services, 1982. Biennial. Free. (Available from French Cultural Services, 972 Fifth Ave., New York, NY 10021.)

Provides general descriptions of the universities in France and their course offerings.

Higher Education in the United Kingdom. London: British Council and the Association of Commonwealth Universities, 1982-84. Biennial. $12.95. (Available from Longman, Inc., 19 W. 44th St., New York, NY 10036.)

Information on degrees, courses, and student life in Great Britain.

How to Live in Britain: The British Council's guide to overseas students and visitors. London: Bell and Hyman, Ltd., with the British Council, 1983. Annual. $3. (Available from Bell and Hyman, Ltd., Denmark House, 37-39 Queen Elizabeth St., London SEW 2Q3, England.)

Useful guide for foreign students planning to study in Britain for the first time. Includes sections on preparations, arrival in Britain, and what to expect once there.

International Jobs: Where they are, how to get them. Eric Kocher. Reading, MA: Addison-Wesley Publishing Co., Inc., 1984. Hardcover, $16.95; paperback, $8.95. (Available from Addison-Wesley Publishing Co., Inc., Jacob Way, Reading, MA 01867.)

A handbook for over 500 career opportunities (including teaching) around the world.

A Librarian's Directory of Exchange Programs, Study Tours, Funding Sources, and Job Opportunities Outside the United States. Diane Stine. Chicago: American Library Association, 1982. (Available from American Library Association, Office for Library Personnel Resources, 50 E. Huron, Chicago, IL 60611.)

Listing of permanent and temporary job exchange situations, as well as study tours abroad designed specifically for librarians.

Multinational Marketing and Employment Directory. 8th ed. New York: World Trade Academy Press, 1982. $90. (Available from World Trade Academy Press, 50 E. 42nd St., New York, NY 10017.)

Listings of American corporations and their branches, subsidiaries, or affiliates in foreign countries. Provides names of corporation presidents, foreign operations officers, and/or personnel directors where available. Notes principal products or services of company. Also includes section for professional and technical personnel seeking employment overseas. Advice on preparation of resumes included.

The Overseas List: Opportunities for living and working in developing countries. David M. Beckman and Elizabeth Anne Donnelly. Minneapolis: Augsburg Publishing House, 1979. $5.50. (Available from Augsburg Publishing House, 426 S. Fifth St., Box 1209, Minneapolis, MN 55440.)

Contains lists and information about church missions, private voluntary development agencies, volunteer-sending agencies, foundations, and international private-development agencies. Additional sections include information about the U.N. system, the U.S. Government, and a separate chapter on study and teaching abroad. Also included is a section on living in the Third World.

Overseas Opportunities for Teachers and Students. Washington, D.C.: National Education Assocation, Office of International Relations, 1983. Free. (Available from NEA, 1201 16th St. NW, Washington, DC 20036.)

Lists publications that assist teachers and students in finding overseas employment.

Resumes for Domestic and Overseas Employment. 2nd ed. New York: World Trade Academy Press, 1977. $15.50. (Available from World Trade Academy Press, 50 E. 42nd St., New York, NY 10017.)

Offers sample resumes and stresses other material required when seeking employment at home or abroad. Discussion and sample of executive contract. Information on employee compensation and fringe benefits for domestic and foreign employment. Includes a list of approximately 250 leading employment recruiters and agencies.

Strategies for Getting an Overseas Job. Kenneth O. Parsons. Babylon, NY: Pilot Industries, Inc., 1983. $3.50. (Available from Pilot Books, 103 Cooper St., Babylon, NY 11702.)

Lists specialized personnel agencies and other sources for locating job opportunities outside the United States. Also offers suggestions for resume and interview preparation.

Summer Jobs in Britain. Susan Griffith, ed. Oxford: Vacation-Work, 1983. Annual. $7.95. (Available from Writer's Digest Books, 9933 Alliance Rd., Cincinnati, OH 45242.)

Comprehensive listing of summer jobs arranged geographically. Includes information on work schedules, descriptions of employment, and salaries.

Teach Overseas: The educator's worldwide handbook and directory to international teaching in overseas schools, colleges, and universities. 1984–85 ed. New York: Maple Tree Publishing, 1984. $12.95. (Available from Maple Tree Publishing, G.P.O. Box 479, New York, NY 10116.)

Teacher's Guide to Overseas Teaching. Louis A. Bajkai, ed. 3rd ed. San Diego: Friends of World Teaching, 1982. $19.95. (Available from Friends of World Teaching, P.O. Box 1049, San Diego, CA 92112.)

Lists sources of information, schools, foreign embassies in the United States, and ministries of education abroad.

Teachers' Guide to Teaching Positions in Foreign Countries. Harold Dilts and Harold W. Hulleman. 1978. (Available from Teaching Positions in Foreign Countries, Box 514, Ames, IA 50010.)

Teaching Opportunities in the Middle East. Washington, DC: America-Mideast Educational and Training Services, Inc. (AMIDEAST), 1983. $5.95. (Available from AMIDEAST, 1717 Massachusetts Ave. NW, Washington, DC 20036.)

Information on contacts for institutions and corporations that hire English-speaking teachers on all levels in the Middle East. Discusses length of contracts, salary range, and visa and degree requirements.

Teaching Opportunities in the Middle East and North Africa. Washington, DC: America-Mideast Educational and Training Services, Inc. (AMIDEAST), 1979. $2. (Available from AMIDEAST, 1717 Massachusetts Ave. NW, Washington, DC 20036.)

Lists organizations and schools recruiting teachers for positions in the Middle East and North Africa. Also covers information on salary, academic requirements, and length of appointment.

Teaching Opportunities Overseas. East Islip, NY: Hill International Publications, 1980. $3. (Available from Hill International Publications, P.O. Box 79, East Islip, NY 11730. Will be out of print in 1985.)

Lists opportunities for teaching abroad. Covers government employment as well as private organizations placing teachers overseas. Lists 100 private schools overseas that employ U.S. teachers.

Work Your Way Around the World. Susan Griffith. Jean Fredette, U.S. ed. Cincinnati: Writer's Digest Books, 1983. $10.95. (Available from Writer's Digest Books, 9933 Alliance Rd., Cincinnati, OH 45242.)

Lists jobs on every continent. Includes information on working a passage, ways to survive when the money runs out, and descriptions of the jobs from people who have had them.

World Study and Travel for Teachers. Richard J. Brett in cooperation with the American Federation of Teachers, AFL-CIO, 1982. 28th ed. $4. (Available from the American Federation of Teachers, AFL-CIO, 11 Dupont Circle NW, Washington, DC 20036.)

YMCA International Division Program Opportunities. 1978. Free. (Available from YMCA International Division, 291 Broadway, New York, NY 10007.)

A listing of YMCA programs abroad, including opportunities for teaching English as a foreign language and camp counseling.

INSTITUTE OF INTERNATIONAL EDUCATION
809 UNITED NATIONS PLAZA, NEW YORK, N.Y. 10017

U.S. REGIONAL OFFICES
MIDWEST
Chicago Sun-Times/Daily News Building
401 North Wabash Avenue/Suite 534/Chicago, Illinois 60611
Tel. (312) 644-1400
NORTHEAST
809 United Nations Plaza/New York, New York 10017
Tel. (212) 883-8422
ROCKY MOUNTAIN
700 Broadway/Suite 112/Denver, Colorado 80203
Tel. (303) 837-0788
SOUTHEAST
133 Carnegie Way, NE,
Suite 900 /Atlanta, Georgia 30303
Tel. (404) 523-7216
SOUTHERN
Suite 1-A, World Trade Center
1520 Texas Avenue/Houston, Texas 77002
Tel. (713) 223-5454
WASHINGTON, D.C.
918 16th Street NW/8th Floor/Washington, D.C. 20006
Tel. (202) 775-0600
WEST COAST
312 Sutter Street/Room 610/San Francisco, California 94108
Tel. (415) 362-6520

OVERSEAS OFFICES
AFRICA
714 Robinson House/Union Avenue and Angwa St./Harare,
Zimbabwe
MEXICO AND CENTRAL AMERICA
Londres 16/Mexico 6, D.F./Mexico **08870037**
Mailing address:
Educational Counseling Center/American Embassy
P.O. Box 3087/Laredo, Texas 78041
SOUTHEAST ASIA
Hong Kong Arts Center/2 Harbour Road–12th Floor/Wanchai/Hong
Kong
Mailing address:
G.P.O. Box 10010/Hong Kong
Branch Office Indonesia, P.O. Box 2079, Jakarta, Indonesia
Branch Office AUA Language Centre–room 219/179 Rajadamri
Road/Bangkok, Thailand
Mailing address:
G.P.O. Box 2050/Bangkok, Thailand

DATE DUE